# Worlds of Change

## Authors, Consultants, and Reviewers

MULTICULTURAL AND EDUCATIONAL CONSULTANTS

Alma Flor Ada, Yvonne Beamer, Joyce Buckner, Helen Gillotte, Cheryl Hudson, Narcita Medina, Lorraine Monroe, James R. Murphy, Sylvia Peña, Joseph B. Rubin, Ramon Santiago, Cliff Trafzer, Hai Tran, Esther Lee Yao

LITERATURE CONSULTANTS

Ashley Bryan, Joan I. Glazer, Paul Janeczko, Margaret H. Lippert

INTERNATIONAL CONSULTANTS

Edward B. Adams, Barbara Johnson, Raymond L. Marshall

MUSIC AND AUDIO CONSULTANTS

John Farrell, Marilyn C. Davidson, Vincent Lawrence, Sarah Pirtle, Susan R. Synder, Rick and Deborah Witkowski, Eastern Sky Media Services, Inc.

TEACHER REVIEWERS

Terry Baker, Jane Bauer, James Bedi, Nora Bickel, Vernell Bowen, Donald Cason, Jean Chaney, Carolyn Clark, Alan Cox, Kathryn DesCarpontrie, Carol L. Ellis, Roberta Gale, Brenda Huffman, Erma Inscore, Sharon Kidwell, Elizabeth Love, Isabel Marcus, Elaine McCraney, Michelle Moraros, Earlene Parr, Dr. Richard Potts, Jeanette Pulliam, Michael Rubin, Henrietta Sakamaki, Kathleen Cultron Sanders, Belinda Snow, Dr. Jayne Steubing, Margaret Mary Sulentic, Barbara Tate, Seretta Vincent, Willard Waite, Barbara Wilson, Veronica York

*Macmillan/McGraw-Hill*

*A Division of The McGraw-Hill Companies*



Macmillan/McGraw-Hill
1221 Avenue of the Americas
New York, New York 10020

Printed in the United States of America

ISBN 0-02-181142-3 / 5, L.11, U.2
1 2 3 4 5 6 7 8 9 RRW 02 01 00 99 98 97

# WORLDS *of* CHANGE

AUTHORS

ELAINE MEI AOKI • VIRGINIA ARNOLD • JAMES FLOOD • JAMES V. HOFFMAN • DIANE LAPP
MIRIAM MARTINEZ • ANNEMARIE SULLIVAN PALINCSAR • MICHAEL PRIESTLEY • CARL B. SMITH
WILLIAM H. TEALE • JOSEFINA VILLAMIL TINAJERO • ARNOLD W. WEBB • KAREN D. WOOD

NEW YORK • FARMINGTON

## Contents

It's Our

## Stories of Young People Who Are Making a Difference

### by Phillip Hoose

# Justin Lebo

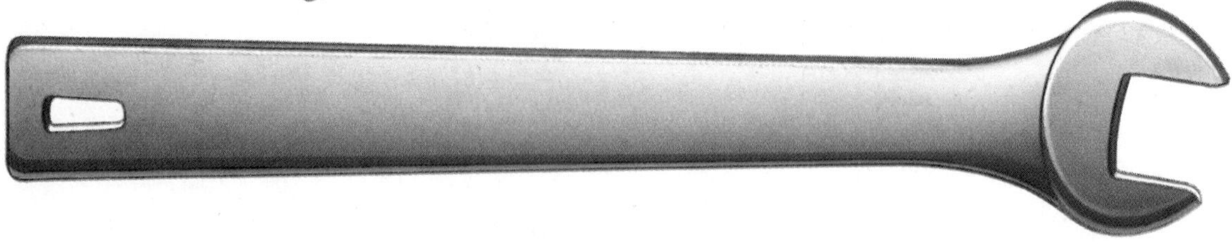

*Since he was ten, Justin Lebo, fourteen, of Paterson, New Jersey, has been building bicycles out of used parts he finds from old junkers. When he finishes, he gives them away to kids who are homeless or sick. He plows most of his allowance into the project and often works on nights and weekends. Why does he do it? The answer is surprising. "In part," he says, "I do it for myself."*

Something about the battered old bicycle at the garage sale caught ten-year-old Justin Lebo's eye. What a wreck! It was like looking at a few big bones in the dust and trying to figure out what kind of dinosaur they had once belonged to.

It was a BMX bike with a twenty-inch frame. Its original color was buried beneath five or six coats of gunky paint. Now it showed up as sort of a rusted red. Everything—the grips, the pedals, the brakes, the seat, the spokes—were bent or broken, twisted and rusted. Justin stood back as if he were inspecting a painting for sale at an auction. Then he made his final judgment: perfect.

Justin talked the owner down to $6.50 and asked his mother, Diane, to help him load the bike into the back of their car.

When he got it home, he wheeled the junker into the garage and showed it proudly to his father. "Will you help me fix it up?" he asked. Justin's hobby was bike racing, a passion the two of them shared. Their garage barely had room for the car anymore.

It was more like a bike shop. Tires and frames hung from hooks on the ceiling, and bike wrenches dangled from the walls.

After every race, Justin and his father would adjust the brakes and realign the wheels of his two racing bikes. This was a lot of work, since Justin raced flat out, challenging every gear and part to perform to its fullest. He had learned to handle almost every repair his father could and maybe even a few things he couldn't. When Justin got really stuck, he went to see Mel, the owner of the best bike shop in town. Mel let him hang out and watch, and he even grunted a few syllables of advice from between the spokes of a wheel now and then.

> *"It is by spending one's self that one becomes rich."*
>
> *Sarah Bernhardt*

Now Justin and his father cleared out a work space in the garage and put the old junker up on a rack. They poured alcohol on the frame and rubbed until the old paint began to yield, layer by layer. They replaced the broken pedal, tightened down a new seat, and restored the grips. In about a week, it looked brand new.

Justin wheeled it out of the garage, leapt aboard, and started off around the block. He stood up and mashed down on the pedals, straining for speed. It was a good, steady ride, but not much of a thrill compared to his racers.

Soon he forgot about the bike. But the very next week, he bought another junker at a yard sale and fixed it up, too. After a while it bothered him that he wasn't really using either bike. Then he realized that what he loved about the old bikes wasn't riding them: it was the challenge of making something new and useful out of something old and broken.

Justin wondered what he should do with them. They were just taking up space in the garage. He

remembered that when he was younger, he used to live near a large brick building called the Kilbarchan Home for Boys. It was a place for boys whose parents couldn't care for them for one reason or another.

He found "Kilbarchan" in the phone book and called the director, who said the boys would be thrilled to get two bicycles. The next day when Justin and his mother unloaded the bikes at the home, two boys raced out to greet them. They leapt aboard the bikes and started tooling around the semicircular driveway, doing wheelies and pirouettes, laughing and shouting.

The Lebos watched them for a while, then started to climb into their car to go home. The boys cried after them, "Wait a minute! You forgot your bikes!" Justin explained that the bikes were for them to keep. "They were so happy," Justin remembers. "It was like they couldn't believe it. It made me feel good just to see them happy."

On the way home, Justin was silent. His mother assumed he was lost in a feeling of satisfaction. But he was thinking about what would happen once those bikes got wheeled inside and everyone saw them. How would all those kids decide who got the bikes? Two bikes could cause more trouble than they would solve. Actually, they hadn't been that hard to build. It was fun. Maybe he could do more. . . .

"Mom," Justin said as they turned onto their street, "I've got an idea. I'm going to make a bike for every boy at Kilbarchan for Christmas." Diane Lebo looked at Justin out of the corner of her eye. She had rarely seen him so determined.

When they got home, Justin called Kilbarchan to find out how many boys lived there. There were twenty-one. It was already June. He had six months to make nineteen bikes. That was almost a bike a week. Justin called the home back to tell them of his plan. "I could tell they didn't think I could do it," Justin remembers. "I knew I could."

## *"It just snowballed."*

Justin knew his best chance was to build bikes almost the way GM or Ford builds cars: in an assembly line. He would start with frames from three-speed, twenty-four-inch BMX bicycles. They were common bikes, and all the parts were interchangeable. If he could find enough decent frames, he could take parts off broken bikes and fasten them onto the good frames. He figured it would take three or four junkers to produce enough parts to make one good bike. That meant sixty to eighty bikes. Where would he get them?

Garage sales seemed to be the only hope. It was June, and there would be garage sales all summer long. But even if he could find that many bikes, how could he ever pay for them? That was hundreds of dollars.

He went to his parents with a proposal. "When Justin was younger, say five or six," says his mother, "he used to give some of his allowance away to help others in need. His father and I would donate a dollar for every dollar Justin donated. So he asked us if it could be like the old days, if we'd match every dollar he put into buying old bikes. We said yes."

Justin and his mother spent most of June and July hunting for cheap bikes at garage sales and thrift shops. They would haul the bikes home, and Justin would start stripping them down in the yard.

***Justin Lebo, who has built hundreds of bikes and given them away to kids who are orphaned, ill, or homeless.***

But by the beginning of August, he had managed to make only ten bikes. Summer vacation was almost over, and school and homework would soon cut into his time. Garage sales would dry up when it got colder, and Justin was out of money. Still, he was determined to find a way.

At the end of August, Justin got a break. A neighbor wrote a letter to the local newspaper describing Justin's project, and an editor thought it would make a good story. One day a reporter entered the Lebo garage. Stepping gingerly through the tires and frames that covered the floor, she found a boy with cut fingers and dirty nails, banging a seat onto a frame. His clothes were covered with grease. In her admiring article about a boy who was devoting his summer to help kids he didn't even know, she said Justin needed bikes and money, and she printed his home phone number.

Overnight, everything changed. "There must have been a hundred calls," Justin says. "People would call me up and ask me to come over and pick up their old bike. Or I'd be working in the garage, and a station wagon would pull up. The driver would leave a couple of bikes by the curb. It just snowballed."

By the start of school, the garage was overflowing with BMX frames. Pyramids of pedals and seats rose in the corners. Soon bike parts filled a toolshed in the backyard and then spilled out into the small yard itself, wearing away the lawn.

*"I don't think you can ever really do anything to help anybody else if it doesn't make you happy."*

*Justin Lebo*

More and more writers and television and radio reporters called for interviews. Each time he told his story, Justin asked for bikes and money. "The first few interviews were fun," Justin says, "but it reached a point where I really didn't like doing them. The publicity was necessary, though. I had to keep doing interviews to get the donations I needed."

By the time school opened, he was working on ten bikes at a time. There were so many calls now that he was beginning to refuse offers that weren't the exact bikes he needed.

As checks came pouring in, Justin's money problems disappeared. He set up a bank account and began to make bulk orders of common parts from Mel's bike shop. Mel seemed delighted to see him. Sometimes, if Justin brought a bike by the shop, Mel would help him fix it. When Justin tried to talk him into a lower price for big orders, Mel smiled and gave in. He respected another good businessman. They became friends.

## "Why do you do it?"

The week before Christmas Justin delivered the last of the twenty-one bikes to Kilbarchan. Once again, the boys poured out of the home and leapt aboard the bikes, tearing around the snow.

And once again, their joy inspired Justin. They reminded him how important bikes were to him. Wheels meant freedom. He thought how much more the freedom to ride must mean to boys like these who had so little freedom in their lives. He decided to keep on building.

"First I made eleven bikes for the children in a foster home my mother told me about. Then I made bikes for all the women in a battered women's shelter. Then I made ten little bikes and tricycles for the kids in a home for children with AIDS. Then I made twenty-three bikes for the Paterson Housing Coalition."

In the four years since he started, Justin Lebo has made between 150 and 200 bikes and given them all away. He has been careful to leave time for his homework, his friends, his coin collection, his new interest in marine biology, and of course his own bikes.

Reporters and interviewers have asked Justin Lebo the same question over and over: "Why do you do it?" The question seems to make him uncomfortable. It's as if they want him to say what a great person he is. Their stories always make him seem like a saint, which he knows he isn't. "Sure it's nice of me to make the bikes," he says, "because I don't have to. But I want to. In part, I do it for myself. I don't think you can ever really do anything to help anybody else if it doesn't make you happy.

"Once I overheard a kid who got one of my bikes say, 'A bike is like a book; it opens up a whole new world.' That's how I feel, too. It made me happy to know that kid felt that way. That's why I do it."

# Dwaina Brooks

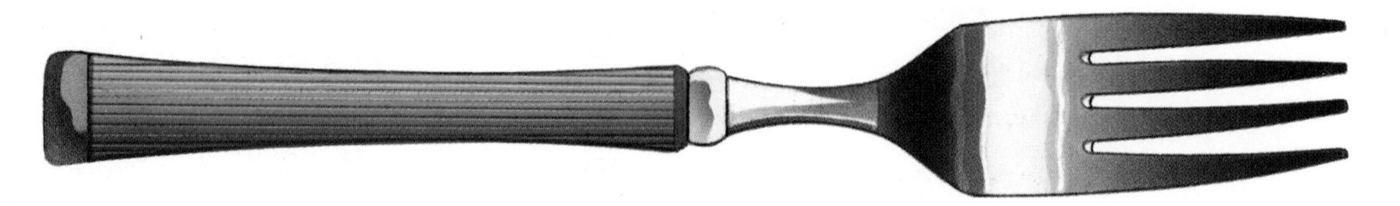

*On Friday nights, Dwaina Brooks, eleven, and as many as twenty-six of her friends and relatives, turn her mother's kitchen into a meal factory for the homeless of Dallas. With the radio set to 100.3—the rap station—and with mayonnaise up to their elbows, they have produced as many as three hundred meals in a night.*

Each morning on her way to school, Dwaina Brooks saw the line of men and women outside a homeless shelter and soup kitchen in Dallas. Many looked cold and sleepy. Sometimes one man stood in the street carrying a sign that said, "I Will Work for Food to Feed My Children." No one ever stopped to talk to him. How could they just pass him by?

At school, her fourth-grade class was doing a unit on homelessness. Once a week, students telephoned a shelter and talked with someone who was staying there. Dwaina would ask the person on the other end of the phone, "How'd you wind up on the streets?" "Do you want to be there?" "What did you do before?" She listened carefully. Most people's lives had been going along okay, and then something bad had happened. They got fired. The family broke up. They couldn't make a rent payment.

Always she asked, "What do you

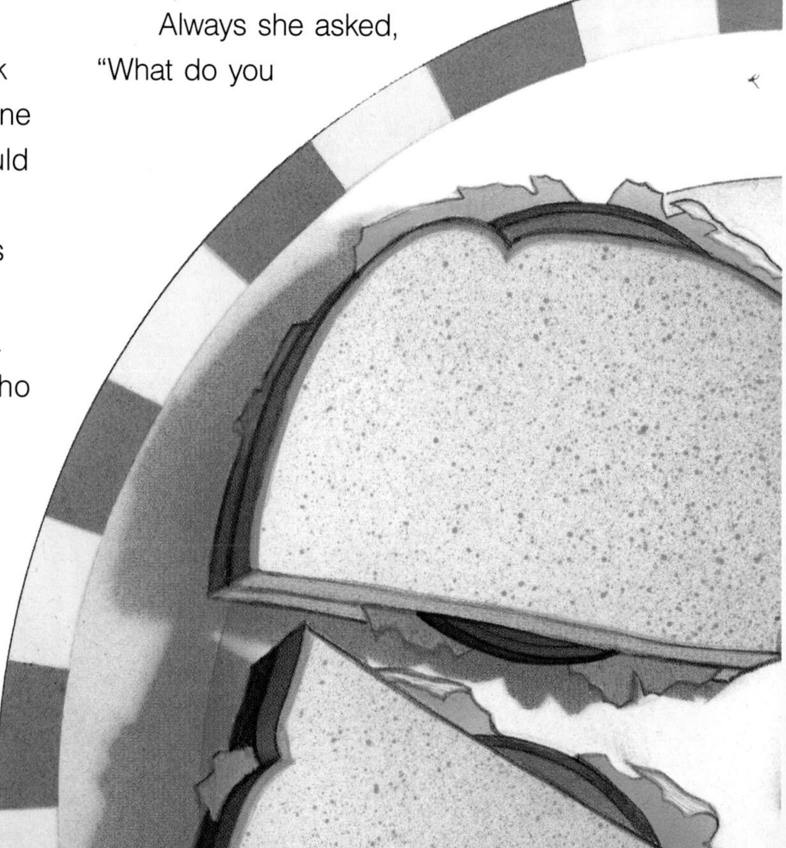

need?" The answer was always "a home," or "a job." It never seemed as though she could do much more than keep sending her lunch money to the shelter. Then one afternoon, Dwaina talked with a young man who had been without a home for a long time.

"What do you need?" she asked him.

"I need a job and a permanent home," he replied.

"Well, I can't give you that," she answered impatiently. "I don't have a job either. Don't you need anything else?"

"Yeah. I would love a really good meal again."

"Well, now," said Dwaina, brightening. "I *can* cook."

> "Even when she was a baby, Dwaina couldn't stand to see anyone hurt . . ."
>
> Gail Brooks

## Why not?

Dwaina tore into the house that night after school and found her mother, Gail. As usual, she was in the kitchen. "Mama," she said. "I need you to help me fix some stuff to take down to that shelter we call at school. Let's make up as much as we can. Sandwiches and chicken. Let's get everyone to do it. C'mon."

Gail Brooks looked at her daughter. All of her children were generous, but Dwaina had always been a little different. Even when she was a baby, Dwaina couldn't stand to see anyone hurt or left out. If she only took one doll to bed with her, pretty soon she would start wondering if all the others felt bad. The next morning, there would be a bed full of dolls and Dwaina on the floor.

Make food for the homeless? Well, why not? They decided to prepare meals on Friday night. They spent the next three days shopping and preparing. Counting Dwaina's lunch money, which she decided to donate to the cause, they figured they had about sixty dollars to spend. Their challenge was how to make that stretch into as many meals as possible.

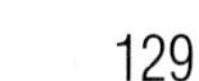

Coupons helped cut the prices for sandwich wrapping, cookies, and mayonnaise. Dwaina's uncle got them discount lunch meats from the store where he used to work. Thursday night was bargain night at the bakery in nearby Lancaster. They drove away with six big loaves of day-old bread for $1.78. "Mama, do you think anyone at the shelter will really eat day-old bread?" Dwaina asked. "We eat it," Gail replied. "If it don't kill us, it won't kill them."

The baker gave them twenty free boxes, too, when he heard how they would be used. Dwaina's aunts and uncles brought over huge sacks of chips and big bottles of salad dressing.

When Dwaina got home from school on Friday, the stage was set. Her mother's table was covered with a plastic cloth. The plastic gloves from the dime store were laid out. Mountains of ham, turkey, and cheese were at one end. Two rows of bread went from one end of the table to the other. They looked like piano keys. A huge jar of mayonnaise was open and ready.

Dwaina's sisters, Stephanie, sixteen, and Crystal, nine, already had aprons tied around their waists. Dwaina turned on the radio, and they all formed an assembly line and dug in. Gail threw chicken into three skillets and got them all going at once. Dwaina slapped meat on open slices of bread and covered them with mayo. Crystal wrapped sandwiches and stuffed sacks. Dwaina looked on proudly as the corner of the kitchen began to fill up with sacks. It looked like a lot of meals.

It was after ten when the last sack was stuffed. The kitchen looked like a tornado had ripped through it. They placed 105 carefully wrapped meals in the bakery boxes, loaded them in the Oldsmobile, and headed downtown.

When they got to the shelter, two men came out to the street and helped carry in the boxes. Dwaina set down her first box and looked around the shelter. It was a big, open room with beds along the walls. It was dark, but some men were up front in a lighted area drinking coffee. She wondered if the man who had said he wanted a good meal was still living there. If he was, she thought with pride, he sure enough would have a treat tomorrow.

## "Who'll be there?"

After that, nearly every Friday night for a year, Dwaina and her mother and

whatever sisters were around made food for shelters in Dallas. At first they took the food to the shelters themselves, but then their church volunteered to make the deliveries for them.

Always, Dwaina wanted to make more meals. That shelter had hundreds of people; she and her mom alone probably weren't feeding half of them. One Friday evening, she had an idea: she knew where she could get some extra help, and lots of it, too.

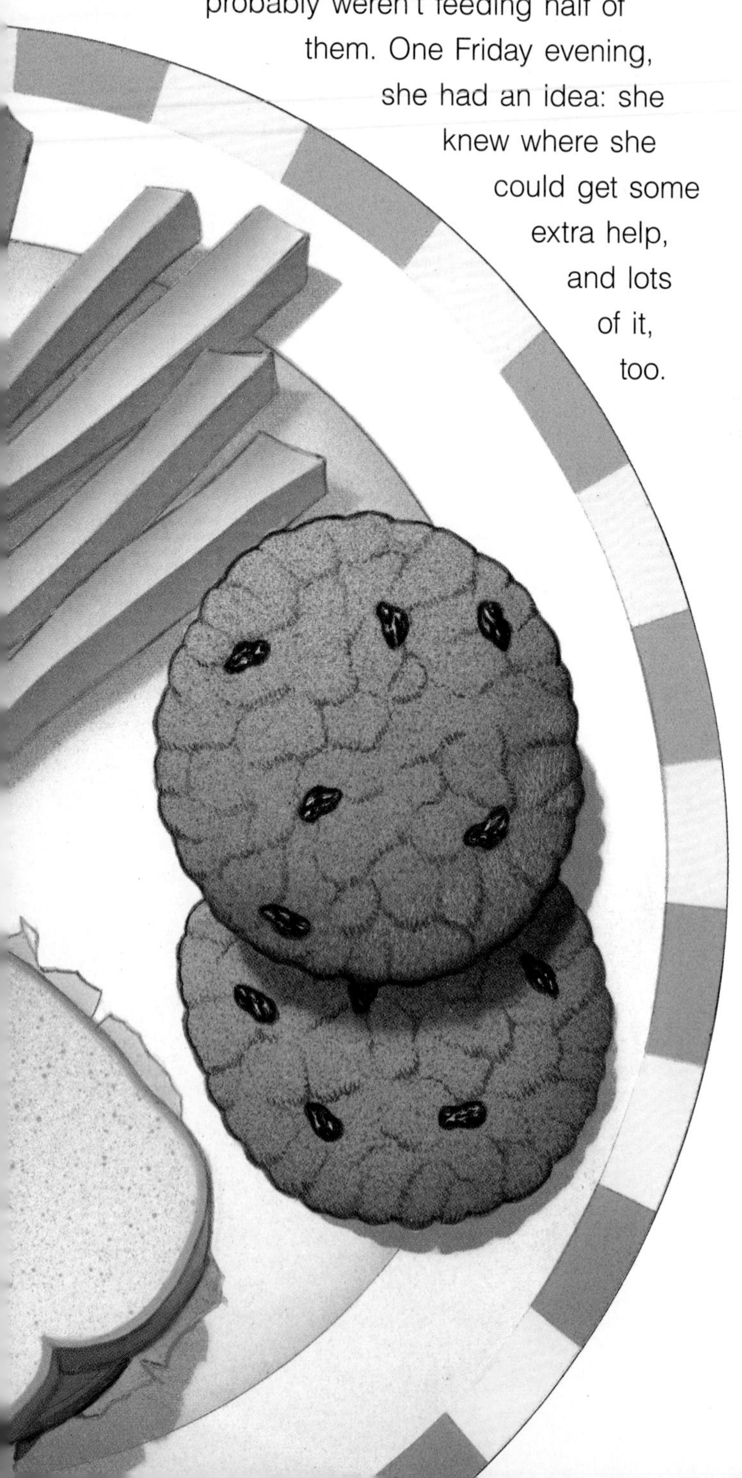

The following Monday, she asked her fifth-grade teacher, Mr. Frost, if she could speak to the class while he took roll. Dwaina had been the class leader since the first day of school, when she had told a group of loud boys to shut up so she could hear her teacher. She could be tough or funny or kind. She always seemed to know exactly what would move them.

Now Dwaina smacked both hands on her desk hard to get their attention and stood up. She pushed her glasses up onto her forehead and glared at them for a moment, hands on hips, as if she were about to lecture them:

"Okay, y'all," she began. "We've been reading about the homeless in class, and I can tell you that for some reason it's getting worse and worse." Her eyes swept around the room. "Now, my mama and I been makin' sandwiches this year till we got mayonnaise up to our elbows and we can't make enough. Why should we be up till midnight every Friday night when y'all ain't doin' a thing? Now, listen. I want you to come to my house this Friday night and help. Who'll be there?"

Twenty-three hands went up. When Dwaina excitedly reported this to her mother, Gail Brooks nearly passed out. "Twenty-three kids? Plus *our* family?" "Yeah, Mama, isn't it great! Think how many meals we can make!"

***Dwaina Brooks, who organized her family and friends to feed homeless people in Dallas.***

Dwaina and Gail advised each participating family about where to get food cheaply. They made a central list of who would bring what and taped it to the refrigerator. All that week, parents drove boxes of food to the Brooks's small house. At school, the kids made bigger and bigger plans each day. Making food for the shelter was shaping up to be the social event of the year.

"Why don't y'all stay over?" asked Dwaina.

"I'll bring popcorn!" said Claire.

"I got a Hammer tape," said Qiana.

"What about boys?" said Christopher. "Can we sleep over, too?"

"Sorry," came a chorus of girls. "Oh, maybe on the kitchen floor."

The next Friday night, twenty-eight people crowded into the Brooks kitchen. They set up one of the world's longest assembly lines, kicked the radio onto 100.3 FM-JAMZ—the rap station—wrapped towels around their waists, and started in. By midnight, the boxes were filled with more than three hundred sacks.

In a little more than two years, Dwaina Brooks, now in sixth grade, has organized several thousand meals for unfortunate people in the Dallas area. She and her mother and the classmates who sometimes still join in have perfected the art of helping others and having fun at the same time. They do it by doing something they already love to do: cooking and putting meals together.

Dwaina hopes to become a doctor and open her own clinic someday, but she thinks it's crazy to wait till then to start caring for others. "Kids should get going," she says. "There aren't enough jobs out there, especially for people without diplomas. Not even at McDonald's. We should try to help. If we don't act, there will be more and more homeless people. Each of us should have some kind of concern in our hearts for other people. And we owe it, too: there isn't a one of us who hasn't been helped by someone."

## Meet
# Phillip Hoose

Phillip Hoose got the idea for *It's Our World, Too!* from his daughter Hannah. She and some classmates held an art sale at their elementary school in Portland, Maine. They sold their own drawings and paintings. The money raised went to a homeless shelter. Hoose says, "Their good work gave me an idea for a book. Why not look all around the world for great stories of young people reaching out, making a difference, trying to help others?"

Hoose spent the next year searching for young people working for positive change. He ended up talking with over a hundred young activists.

When Hoose is not writing, he himself also works to change the world. He raises money for a group that tries to save prairies, swamps, marshes, and forests from being destroyed.

# MAKING A DIFFERENCE

by Tracy Williams Cheney and Connie Eden

This is a story about kids who saved a green space in our neighborhood. We are the two grown-ups who worked with them and want to share their excellent work with you.

We live in the state of Washington. Most people think of tall green trees when they think of our state. But every year, more and more forests disappear to make room for houses and shopping malls. The population of our city, Everett, is expected to be almost twice as big in the next 20 years. We already have 75,000 people and not enough parks or green spaces.

On a map of our neighborhood, we had discovered some wooded land owned by the city. We checked and found that there was no money, time, or staff to make or take care of a new park. We tried to interest the adults at our neighborhood meetings, but no one seemed to care.

Then, a classroom of students at View Ridge Elementary School and their teacher jumped in and helped us.

For many years, neighbors had dumped yard clippings and garbage on this property. There is a creek that runs through here only during heavy rain—and then it flows into a salmon stream. A developer planned to build 15 houses squeezed between this land and our grade school. His plans would mean oily water running off the new streets and driveways into the creek.

The class did some investigating. They took a boat trip and saw how human activities on land can cause problems for aquatic animals and fish. For example, clear-cutting trees causes muddy streams because rain washes huge amounts of dirt down the bare hillsides. This clogs the air supply for fish, and salmon can't survive. The class visited the Public Works Department to learn

**The kids learned about native plants and "invaders" such as holly. Natives are the original plants in a region. Invaders were brought in by people and animals. In Everett, there's lots of holly. Birds eat the berries and spread the seeds through their droppings.**

how water is controlled and filtered in a city. When the developer realized people cared about the creek, he paid for a new design for collecting dirty water on his property.

The students divided into teams. Adults with special knowledge about wildlife, plants, and water came to school to talk to the children. The class collected this information and made a scrapbook for future classes.

Each student adopted a tree, named it, drew pictures of it, and wrote poems about it. They listened through stethoscopes to the sap running.

Next came the trash cleanup—a week-long job. The kids found everything from fake fingernails to chunks of concrete. Then, on a Saturday morning, 44 people, including neighbors and parents, joined in to fill a dumpster. The city paid for removing tons of garbage and provided a machine to cut up fallen trees. The kids spread fresh wood chips along the pathways.

The project was humongous.

Finally, it was time to name the park. The class discovered that two women—Gertrude Johnston and Cora Kelly—had donated the land for a park in the 1920s. The land had been forgotten and neglected all this time. All fourth and fifth graders at the school voted. The winning name was "Johnston/Kelly Environmental Park."

A group of students presented the name at our neighborhood meeting and it was approved. Next, they needed to convince

**Kids, parents, neighbors, teachers, and city workers pitched in on the day of the cleanup. They gathered tons of garbage.**

the park board, the city council, and the mayor. Two boys spent hours investigating records at the library, county courthouse, and even the cemetery to help show that these two women's names should be used for the park.

The developer now gives money to help protect the park. With this money, the class will put up signs identifying plant species. They will plant native plants, buy guide books, and make a space for an outdoor classroom. Our neighborhood organization will pay for a sign that says "Johnston/Kelly Environmental Park."

Here in Everett, kids did what grown-ups wouldn't do. They saved a wildlife area and green space. And they gave a life-long gift to our neighborhood.

# Jigsaw PUZZLE

My beautiful picture of pirates and treasure
Is spoiled, and almost I don't want to start
To put it together; I've lost all the pleasure
I used to find in it: there's one missing part.

I know there's one missing—they lost it, the others,
The last time they played with my puzzle—and maybe
There's more than one missing: along with the brothers
And sisters who borrow my toys there's the baby.

There's a hole in the ship or the sea that it sails on,
And I said to my father, "Well, what shall I do?
It isn't the same now that some of it's gone."
He said, "Put it together; the world's like that too."

RUSSELL HOBAN

# New Pro

# vidence

## a changing cityscape

by Renata von Tscharner and Ronald Lee Fleming

illustrated by Denis Orloff

# 1910

*Put the city up; tear the city down;*
*put it up again; let us find a city. . . .*
*—Carl Sandburg*

New Providence is thriving. Cobblestone streets bustle with activity—Model T Fords, streetcars, and horse-drawn carts carrying meat, milk, and ice. There is no concert in the bandstand today, but a crowd has gathered in the square in front of the Town Hall and the Tenebo County Courthouse. A fountain has been built in commemoration of Chief Tenebo, a Native American from a local tribe. The statue is about to be unveiled. Around the

base of the fountain is an inscription: GOOD CITIZENS ARE THE RICHES OF A CITY.

New Providence's good citizens—women in long skirts and men in hats—buy fruit at the sidewalk stand in front of the grocery and most of their clothing and household items at Getz & McClure's, the largest store in town. They shop for shoes and jewelry and office supplies and have supper at Gilman's or at the Butler House Cafe.

The rural hillsides surrounding the city are lush, with comfortable Victorian homes dotting the landscape and the Bloom mill and worker housing in the distance. The large red brick schoolhouse is attended by all school-age children in the region. A flock of birds flies peacefully overhead.

# 1935

As a mist rolls into New Providence, effects of the Great Depression are visible; the city has fallen on hard times. Gone is the bandstand from the courthouse square, where homeless men now huddle over trash can fires for warmth. A WPA sign publicizes the Works Progress Administration, a jobs program funded by the government. A line of jobless men waits for free bread outside the post office, and hoboes are taking a free ride out of the city on trains. Many buildings are in need of repair.

But even in times such as these, life goes on. A Charlie Chaplin movie is playing at the Strand Theater. A huge Coca-Cola advertisement goes up on the side of a building. A streetlight now controls automobile traffic. The Bloom mill—expanded before the stock market crash—is still in operation, the grocery has become a shoe store, and the dry goods store, a jeweler's. The Colonel Fleming House now accommodates three small businesses. Art Deco chrome and glass streamline some of the storefronts, contrasting with the older styles of the upper stories. A modern yellow apartment building squats on the hillside, while a biplane and a blimp cruise the skies.

# 1955

**A** postwar prosperity settles over New Providence, although there are signs that downtown is deteriorating.

The night sky glows with neon, Christmas lights, and lighted billboards advertising bread, used cars, and cigarettes. Part of the courthouse square is now paved with asphalt to make room for more and larger cars. Buses have replaced streetcars. Franchises like Rexall's and Woolworth's have moved into town, and the Alpine Motel attracts traveling businessmen. Walt Disney's *Lady and the Tramp* is playing at the Strand.

The elegant Butler House is now a liquor store and a boarding house for transients. Next to it, a Victorian cast-iron building is being covered with prefabricated siding. Getz & McClure's has already been sheathed with stark metal grillwork and a currently popular style of lettering. Two of the small businesses in the Colonel Fleming House are boarded up. Behind it, a bland new building has been erected to house Monarch Insurance. The old slate roof of the Town Hall has been replaced by asphalt shingles. A fire is raging at the train station, while the citizens of New Providence go about their holiday shopping.

# 1970

By 1970, downtown New Providence is an uninspired jumble of old and new. To attract people from thriving suburbia, part of Main Street has been converted into a pedestrian mall, dominated by a harsh concrete fountain. But there is less traffic than ever in the city center, and fewer people actually live there.

A number of people in town today are gathered outside the courthouse, taking part in a protest march against the Vietnam War. Across the newly sunken and cemented square, a mugging is in progress. Graffiti mars the area, as do more and more billboards—advertising beer, cigarettes, whiskey, and an Army/Navy surplus

store. The post office and several other buildings have been demolished and turned into parking lots, the Bloom mill is for rent, and the train station tower remains burnt out.

The Alpine Motel is now a Holiday Inn, a Fotomat has opened, and the Beatles' *Let It Be* is playing at the Strand. A day school has opened, complete with colorful murals and giant toad-stools. The Colonel Fleming House seems about to be rescued by a preservation group. Victorian homes in the hills are disappearing to make room for highways, look-alike suburban housing, and another addition to the school. In the afternoon sky, a jet flies over the increasing number of powerlines strung across the horizon.

# 1980

Ten years later, there are signs that downtown New Providence is sadly in need of recovery—and also signs that help is on the way.

Chief Tenebo's statue has been vandalized; debris blows around its dry base and across the square. Graffiti is everywhere, street lamps are smashed, and a police box has appeared. The Colonel Fleming House has been moved across the street, but its placement does not look permanent. In its old location are a Cor-Ten steel sculpture and Monarch Insurance's new highrise, which bears no architectural relationship to the buildings around it.

1980 1980 1980 1980 1980

But the streets seem more populated, and people are again living—even barbecuing—downtown in the new red brick infill structure next to McDonald's. The only billboard in town advertises health food and a cultural event. The old Strand Theater is being expanded into a Cultural Center. And although the Butler House has been all but abandoned, a sign shows that rehabilitation is being planned. A superhighway now cuts through the hillside, making downtown more accessible to summer holiday travelers. A large parking structure has been built, and well-tended plantings soften the mall.

# 1992

*It is wisdom to think the people are the city. . . .*

*—Carl Sandburg*

In the sunny afternoon sky a flock of birds heads back to its winter home. Below, people have returned to the city—living, shopping, working, playing. New Providence has never looked better. Sidewalk vendors sell their produce once more, and traffic again flows through handsomely paved streets. Buses are made to look like old-fashioned trolleys. Chief Tenebo has been restored, and the bandstand is back, a concert in full swing. Gone are graffiti, billboards, and harsh sculptures. Plants and fall flowers are everywhere—even the parking structure has been elegantly camouflaged.

92 1992 1992 1992 1992 1

All of the old building facades have been renovated, and the condition of most buildings is strikingly similar to what it was in 1910. The Town Hall's slate roof has been restored, and the air-raid siren is gone. Street furniture is comfortable and compatible with the architecture. The circular clock is back in front of the Butler House, now beautifully refurbished. An arcaded building where people live and work occupies the site of the controversial tower, serving as an entry into the restored train station, and an atrium full of plants softens the Monarch Insurance skyscraper. A Fitness Center has replaced the Feminist Health Center, and a film festival is in progress at the Strand Cultural Center.

The good citizens of New Providence have worked hard to make the city livable again—and true to its heritage.

*New Providence, a small American city, will not be found on any map. It is the creation of a team of architectural historians and designers, and yet its fictional cityscape is truly authentic. The buildings, the signs, even the street furniture can be found somewhere in urban America. Almost every detail was discovered in old photographs and assembled by the design team at The Townscape Institute.*

**Baltimore, Maryland**
(McDonald's building and $H_2O$ fountain)

**Binghamton, New York**
(courthouse lights)

**Boston, Massachusetts**
(church in center and 1970 concrete plaza)

**Brookline, Massachusetts**
(church)

**Cambridge, Massachusetts**
(signs)

**Chelsea, Massachusetts**
(storefront)

**Chicago, Illinois**
(metal awning on the Butler House)

**Cincinnati, Ohio**
(1987 City Identity System booth)

**Denver, Colorado**
(building across the street from courthouse in 1910)

**Eugene, Oregon**
(1970 modern concrete fountain)

**Flint, Michigan**
(1910 shoe sign and street awnings)

**Fresno, California**
(1970-80 sculptural clock tower)

**Garland, Utah**
(Bloom mill)

**Grand Rapids, Michigan**
(City Hall)

**Heber City, Utah**
(water tower)

**Junction City, Kansas**
(corner bank)

**Knoxville, Tennessee**
(billboard)

**Los Angeles, California**
(Getz & McClure building)

**Milwaukee, Wisconsin**
(suburban villas)

**Montclair, New Jersey**
(Colonel Fleming House)

**Montgomery, Alabama**
(Victorian cast-iron building)

**New York, New York**
(Butler House and train station)

**Portland, Oregon**
(fountain base)

**Richmond, Virginia**
(signs on Reiter's shoe store)

**Salem, Ohio**
(cornice on Main Street)

**San Diego, California**
(circular clock)

**Scottsdale, Arizona**
(parking structure with plantings)

**Staunton, Virginia**
(stained glass in McDonald's building)

**Syracuse, New York**
(layout of courthouse square)

**Topeka, Kansas**
(Alpine Motel sign)

**Townsend, Massachusetts**
(bandstand)

**Traverse City, Michigan**
(mansard roof on Butler House)

**Upper Sandusky, Ohio**
(horse fountain and pavilion)

**Waltham, Massachusetts**
(bench)

**Washington, D.C.**
(Masonic building)

**Westerville, Ohio**
(gas station)

**Wilkes-Barre, Pennsylvania**
(park outline)

**Wilmington, Delaware**
(1970 metal Main Street shelters)

**Winooski, Vermont**
(Main Street building)

*Meet*
# Renata von Tscharner *and* Ronald Lee Fleming

Have you ever wanted to design your very own town? That's what Renata von Tscharner and Ronald Lee Fleming did. Both are city planners, people who help make the buildings, parks, and streets more pleasant and usable for residents.

After they were married in 1979, von Tscharner and Fleming founded the Townscape Institute in Cambridge, Massachusetts. Through the institute, they encourage young people to become involved in their own communities, because they believe children can make a difference in how those communities look and change.

That's one of the reasons they wrote *New Providence: A Changing Cityscape*. "I am constantly trying to get children to use their eyes [and to wonder], 'Why is something the way it is and how could I change it?'" says Fleming.

# CITY

In the morning the city
Spreads its wings
Making a song
In stone that sings.

In the evening the city
Goes to bed
Hanging lights
About its head.

**Langston Hughes**

# Meet Alma Flor Ada

"Most of my stories I told aloud before I ever wrote them down," says Alma Flor Ada. "And it was other people listening and other people being interested that gave me a motivation to write them."

Listening to other people's stories has also influenced Ada's writing. *The Gold Coin* is based in part on a story her grandfather told her when she was about fifteen. In the story, a rich man had to choose between going away to save his fortune or staying with his dying wife. That man was Alma Flor Ada's grandfather—and he told her he never regretted choosing to stay with his wife. "[Money] should never rule your life," he told her.

Alma Flor Ada grew up in Cuba and today lives in California, where she is a professor of multicultural education at the University of San Francisco. She has written many children's books published in Mexico, Peru, Argentina, and Spain.

# THE GOLD COIN

by Alma Flor Ada

illustrated by Neil Waldman

translated from the Spanish by Bernice Randall

Juan had been a thief for many years. Because he did his stealing by night, his skin had become pale and sickly. Because he spent his time either hiding or sneaking about, his body had become shriveled and bent. And because he had neither friend nor relative to make him smile, his face was always twisted into an angry frown.

One night, drawn by a light shining through the trees, Juan came upon a hut. He crept up to the door and through a crack saw an old woman sitting at a plain, wooden table.

What was that shining in her hand? Juan wondered. He could not believe his eyes: It was a gold coin. Then he heard the woman say to herself, "I must be the richest person in the world."

Juan decided instantly that all the woman's gold must be his. He thought that the easiest thing to do was to watch until the woman left. Juan hid in the bushes and huddled under his poncho, waiting for the right moment to enter the hut.

Juan was half asleep when he heard knocking at the door and the sound of insistent voices. A few minutes later, he saw the woman, wrapped in a black cloak, leave the hut with two men at her side.

Here's my chance! Juan thought. And, forcing open a window, he climbed into the empty hut.

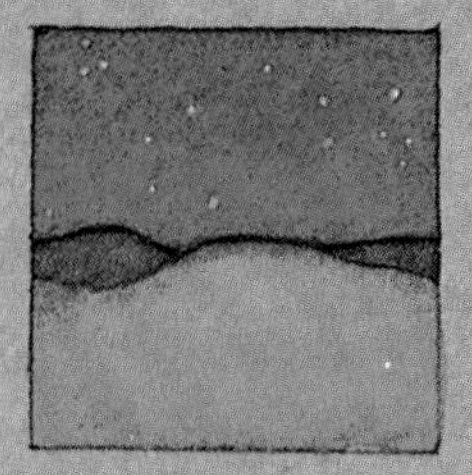

He looked about eagerly for the gold. He looked under the bed. It wasn't there. He looked in the cupboard. It wasn't there, either. Where could it be? Close to despair, Juan tore away some beams supporting the thatch roof.

Finally, he gave up. There was simply no gold in the hut.

All I can do, he thought, is to find the old woman and make her tell me where she's hidden it.

So he set out along the path that she and her two companions had taken.

It was daylight by the time Juan reached the river. The countryside had been deserted, but here, along the riverbank, were two huts. Nearby, a man and his son were hard at work, hoeing potatoes.

It had been a long, long time since Juan had spoken to another human being. Yet his desire to find the woman was so strong that he went up to the farmers and asked, in a hoarse, raspy voice, "Have you seen a short, gray-haired woman, wearing a black cloak?"

"Oh, you must be looking for Doña Josefa," the young boy said. "Yes, we've seen her. We went to fetch her this morning, because my grandfather had another attack of—"

"Where is she now?" Juan broke in.

"She is long gone," said the father with a smile. "Some people from across the river came looking for her, because someone in their family is sick."

"How can I get across the river?" Juan asked anxiously.

"Only by boat," the boy answered. "We'll row you across later, if you'd like." Then turning back to his work, he added, "But first we must finish digging up the potatoes."

The thief muttered, "Thanks." But he quickly grew impatient. He grabbed a hoe and began to help the pair of farmers. The sooner we finish, the sooner we'll get across the river, he thought. And the sooner I'll get to my gold!

It was dusk when they finally laid down their hoes. The soil had been turned, and the wicker baskets were brimming with potatoes.

"Now can you row me across?" Juan asked the father anxiously.

"Certainly," the man said. "But let's eat supper first."

Juan had forgotten the taste of a home-cooked meal and the pleasure that comes from sharing it with others. As he sopped up the last of the stew with a chunk of dark bread, memories of other meals came back to him from far away and long ago.

By the light of the moon, father and son guided their boat across the river.

"What a wonderful healer Doña Josefa is!" the boy told Juan. "All she had to do to make Abuelo better was give him a cup of her special tea."

"Yes, and not only that," his father added, "she brought him a gold coin."

Juan was stunned. It was one thing for Doña Josefa to go around helping people. But how could she go around handing out gold coins—*his gold coins?*

When the threesome finally reached the other side of the river, they saw a young man sitting outside his hut.

"This fellow is looking for Doña Josefa," the father said, pointing to Juan.

"Oh, she left some time ago," the young man said.

"Where to?" Juan asked tensely.

"Over to the other side of the mountain," the young man replied, pointing to the vague outline of mountains in the night sky.

"How did she get there?" Juan asked, trying to hide his impatience.

"By horse," the young man answered. "They came on horseback to get her because someone had broken his leg."

"Well, then, I need a horse, too," Juan said urgently.

"Tomorrow," the young man replied softly. "Perhaps I can take you tomorrow, maybe the next day. First I must finish harvesting the corn."

So Juan spent the next day in the fields, bathed in sweat from sunup to sundown.

Yet each ear of corn that he picked seemed to bring him closer to his treasure. And later that evening, when he helped the young man husk several ears so they could boil them for supper, the yellow kernels glittered like gold coins.

While they were eating, Juan thought about Doña Josefa. Why, he wondered, would someone who said she was the world's richest woman spend her time taking care of every sick person for miles around?

The following day, the two set off at dawn. Juan could not recall when he last had noticed the beauty of the sunrise. He felt strangely moved by the sight of the mountains, barely lit by the faint rays of the morning sun.

As they neared the foothills, the young man said, "I'm not surprised you're looking for Doña Josefa. The whole countryside needs her. I went for her because my wife had been running a high fever. In no time at all, Doña Josefa had her on the road to recovery. And what's more, my friend, she brought her a gold coin!"

Juan groaned inwardly. To think that someone could hand out gold so freely! What a strange woman Doña Josefa is, Juan thought. Not only is she willing to help one person after another, but she doesn't mind traveling all over the countryside to do it!

"Well, my friend," said the young man finally, "this is where I must leave you. But you don't have far to walk. See that house over there? It belongs to the man who broke his leg."

The young man stretched out his hand to say good-bye. Juan stared at it for a moment. It had been a long, long time since the thief had shaken hands with anyone. Slowly, he pulled out a hand from under his poncho. When his companion grasped it firmly in his own, Juan felt suddenly warmed, as if by the rays of the sun.

But after he thanked the young man, Juan ran down the road. He was still eager to catch up with Doña Josefa. When he reached the house, a woman and a child were stepping down from a wagon.

"Have you seen Doña Josefa?" Juan asked.

"We've just taken her to Don Teodosio's," the woman said. "His wife is sick, you know—"

"How do I get there?" Juan broke in. "I've got to see her."

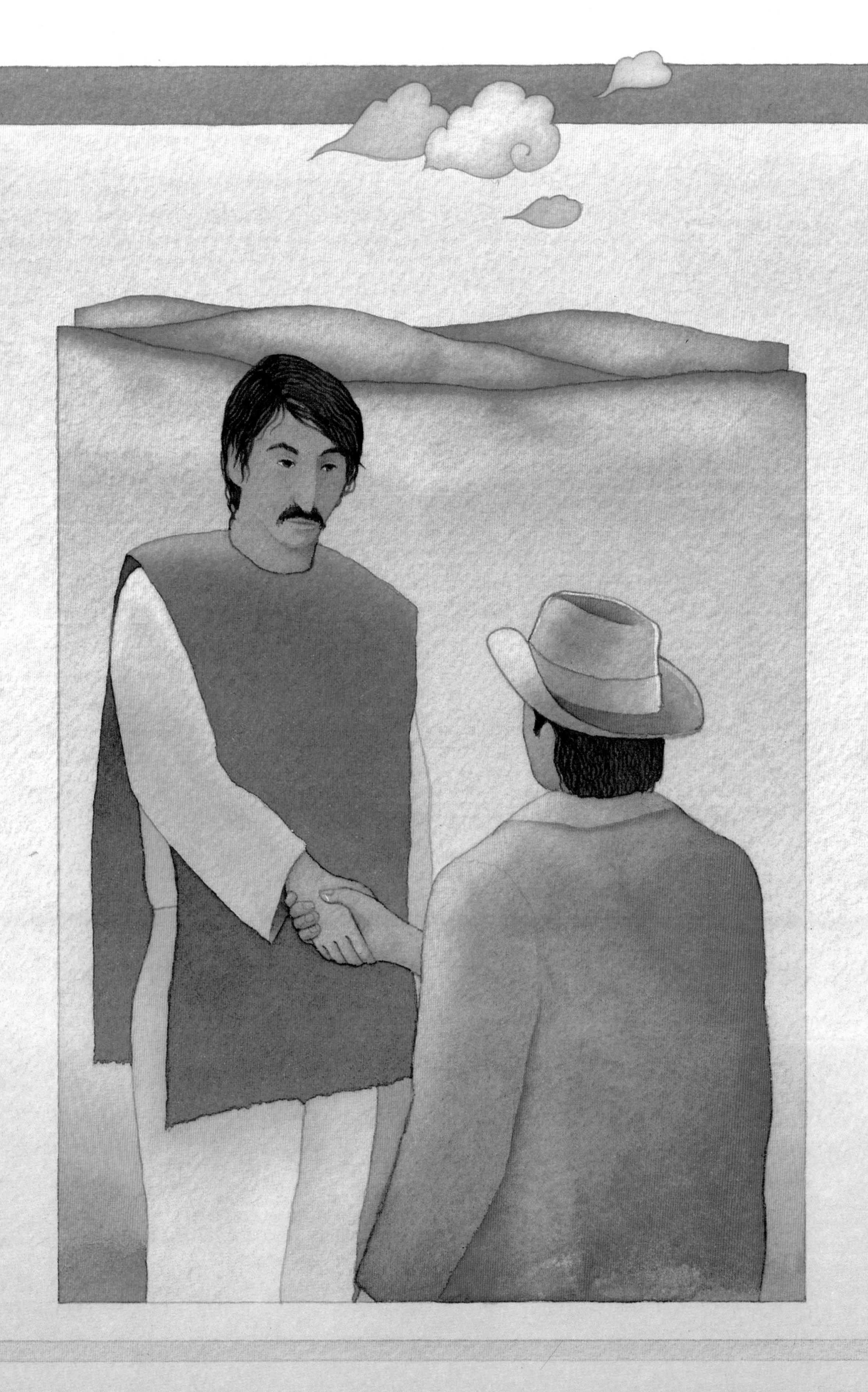

"It's too far to walk," the woman said amiably. "If you'd like, I'll take you there tomorrow. But first I must gather my squash and beans."

So Juan spent yet another long day in the fields. Working beneath the summer sun, Juan noticed that his skin had begun to tan. And although he had to stoop down to pick the squash, he found that he could now stretch his body. His back had begun to straighten, too.

Later, when the little girl took him by the hand to show him a family of rabbits burrowed under a fallen tree, Juan's face broke into a smile. It had been a long, long time since Juan had smiled.

Yet his thoughts kept coming back to the gold.

The following day, the wagon carrying Juan and the woman lumbered along a road lined with coffee fields.

The woman said, "I don't know what we would have done without Doña Josefa. I sent my daughter to our neighbor's house, who then brought Doña Josefa on horseback. She set my husband's leg and then showed me how to brew a special tea to lessen the pain."

Getting no reply, she went on. "And, as if that weren't enough, she brought him a gold coin. Can you imagine such a thing?"

Juan could only sigh. No doubt about it, he thought, Doña Josefa is someone special. But Juan didn't know whether to be happy that Doña Josefa had so much gold she could freely hand it out, or angry for her having already given so much of it away.

When they finally reached Don Teodosio's house, Doña Josefa was already gone. But here, too, there was work that needed to be done. . . .

Juan stayed to help with the coffee harvest. As he picked the red berries, he gazed up from time to time at the trees that grew, row upon row, along the hill-sides. What a calm, peaceful place this is! he thought.

The next morning, Juan was up at daybreak. Bathed in the soft, dawn light, the mountains seemed to smile at him. When Don Teodosio offered him a lift on horseback, Juan found it difficult to have to say good-bye.

"What a good woman Doña Josefa is!" Don Teodosio said, as they rode down the hill toward the sugarcane fields. "The minute she heard about my wife being sick, she came with her special herbs. And as if that weren't enough, she brought my wife a gold coin!"

In the stifling heat, the kind that often signals the approach of a storm, Juan simply sighed and mopped his brow. The pair continued riding for several hours in silence.

Juan then realized he was back in familiar territory, for they were now on the stretch of road he had traveled only a week ago—though how much longer it now seemed to him. He jumped off Don Teodosio's horse and broke into a run.

This time the gold would not escape him! But he had to move quickly, so he could find shelter before the storm broke.

Out of breath, Juan finally reached Doña Josefa's hut. She was standing by the door, shaking her head slowly as she surveyed the ransacked house.

"So I've caught up with you at last!" Juan shouted, startling the old woman. "Where's the gold?"

"The gold coin?" Doña Josefa said, surprised and looking at Juan intently. "Have you come for the gold coin? I've been trying hard to give it to someone who might need it," Doña Josefa said. "First to an old man who had just gotten over a bad attack. Then to a young woman who had been running a fever. Then to a man with a broken leg. And finally to Don Teodosio's wife. But none of them would take it. They all said, 'Keep it. There must be someone who needs it more.'"

Juan did not say a word.

"You must be the one who needs it," Doña Josefa said.

She took the coin out of her pocket and handed it to him. Juan stared at the coin, speechless.

At that moment a young girl appeared, her long braid bouncing as she ran. "Hurry, Doña Josefa, please!" she said breathlessly. "My mother is all alone, and the baby is due any minute."

"Of course, dear," Doña Josefa replied. But as she glanced up at the sky, she saw nothing but black clouds. The storm was nearly upon them. Doña Josefa sighed deeply.

"But how can I leave now? Look at my house! I don't know what has happened to the roof. The storm will wash the whole place away!"

And there was a deep sadness in her voice.

Juan took in the child's frightened eyes, Doña Josefa's sad, distressed face, and the ransacked hut.

"Go ahead, Doña Josefa," he said. "Don't worry about your house. I'll see that the roof is back in shape, good as new."

The woman nodded gratefully, drew her cloak about her shoulders, and took the child by the hand. As she turned to leave, Juan held out his hand.

"Here, take this," he said, giving her the gold coin. "I'm sure the newborn will need it more than I."

# Money, Money, Money

## Bartering

A long time ago people didn't need money. They got everything they needed through bartering, or trading. In bartering, you trade something you don't need for something you do need. Bartering is great as long as somebody wants the things that you have.

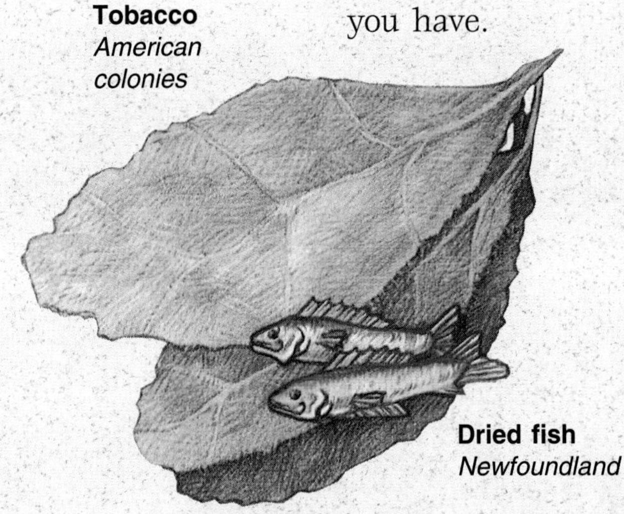

**Tobacco**
*American colonies*

**Dried fish**
*Newfoundland*

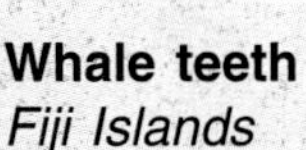

**Whale teeth**
*Fiji Islands*

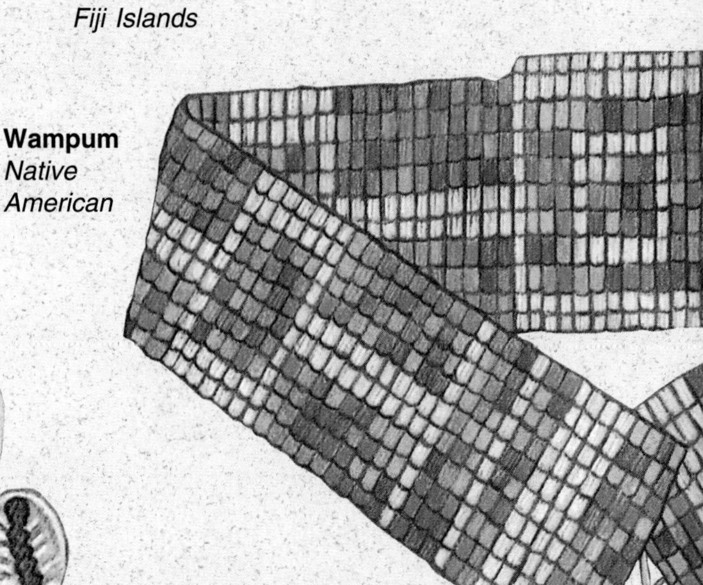

**Wampum**
*Native American*

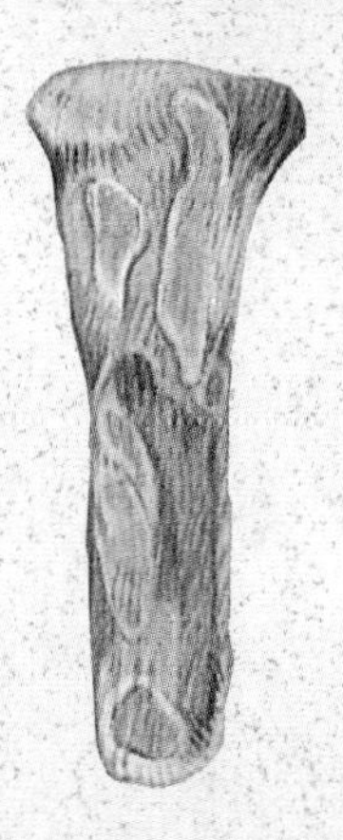

**Money axe**
*Mexico*

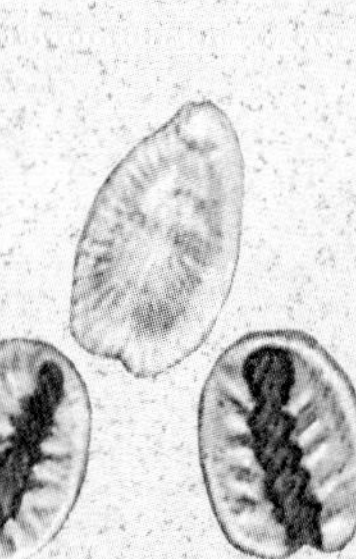

**Cowrie shells**
*China*

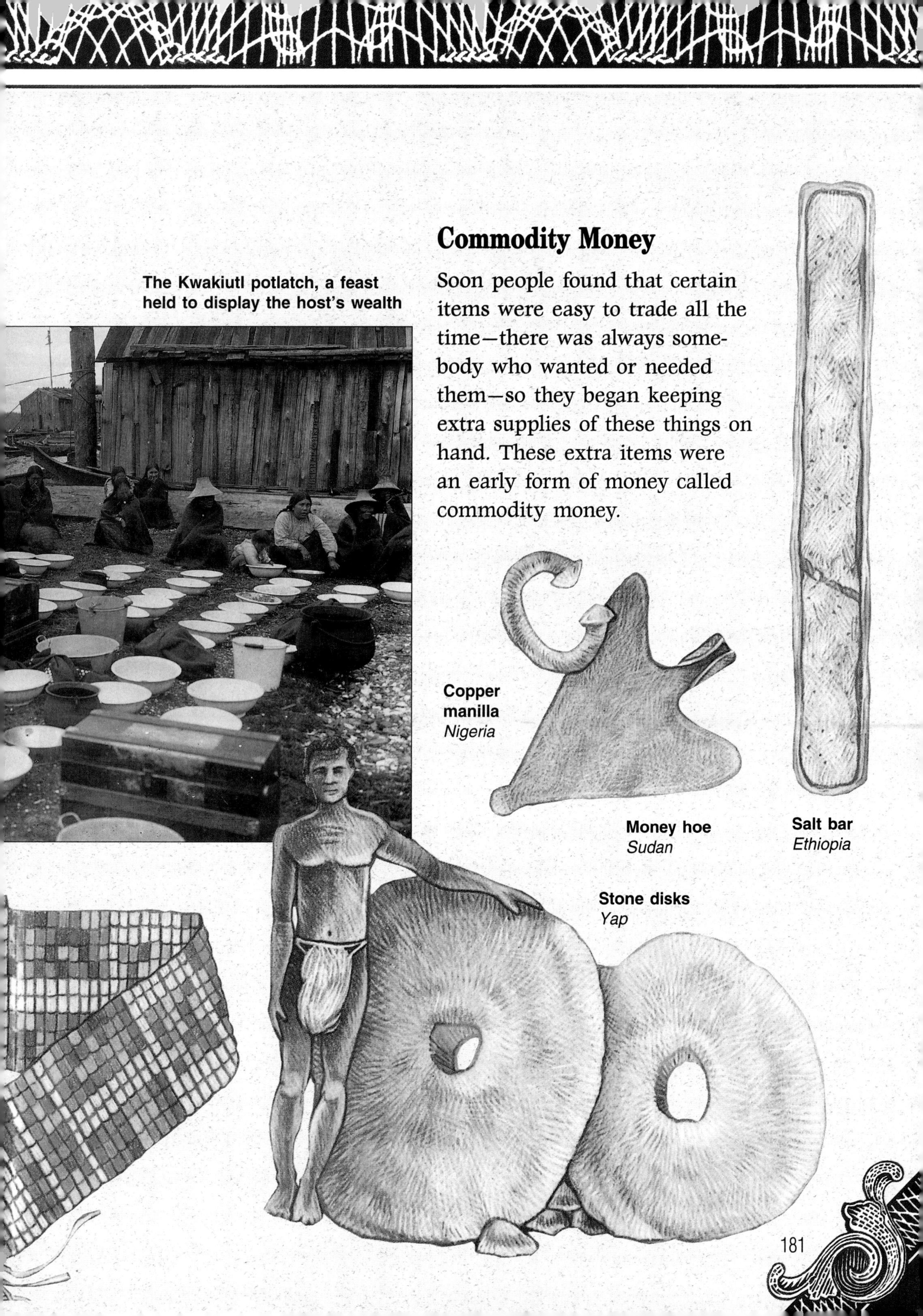


## Commodity Money

Soon people found that certain items were easy to trade all the time—there was always somebody who wanted or needed them—so they began keeping extra supplies of these things on hand. These extra items were an early form of money called commodity money.

The Kwakiutl potlatch, a feast held to display the host's wealth

## Metal Money

After a while people began to use pieces of metal—copper, bronze, iron, silver, and gold—instead of commodities as money. Metal was better to use because:

- it was easier to carry
- it wouldn't rot or spoil
- it was easy to recognize
- it wouldn't wear out easily
- it was scarce enough to be valuable
- it wouldn't break

When people began to use metal for money, they measured it out in lumps, bars, and rings. The heavier the piece of metal, the more a person could buy with it. But that meant that every time you went shopping, someone had to weigh your metal.

Soon someone discovered that you could melt metal down into disks and mark their weight on them, then use them over and over. These disks were the first coins.

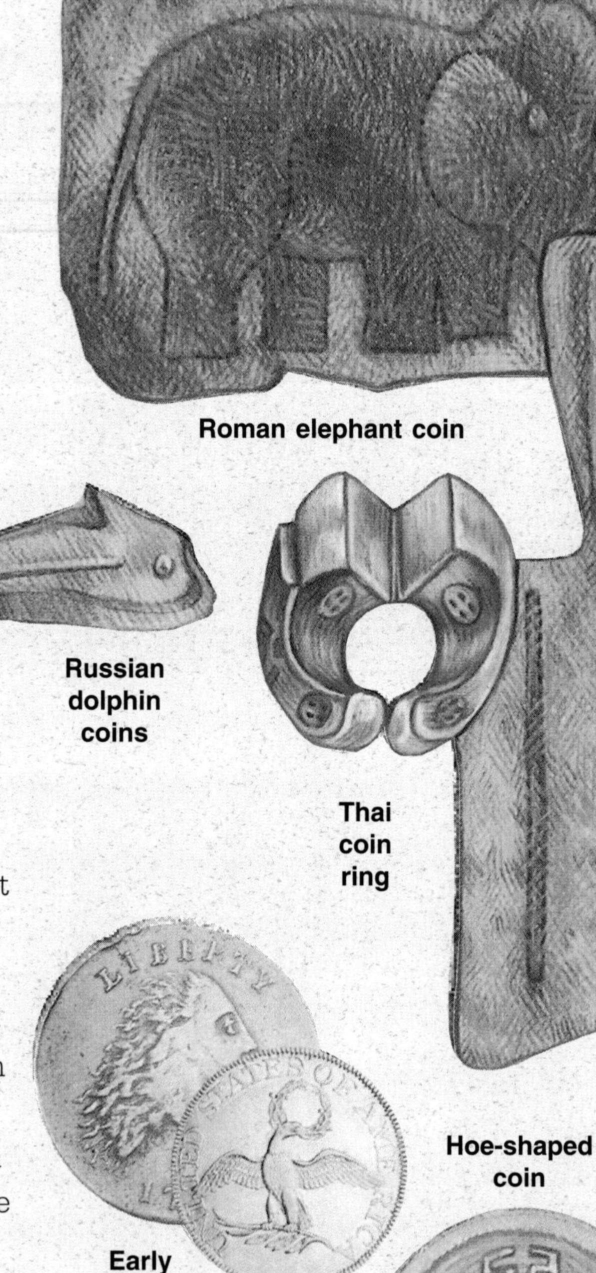

Roman elephant coin

Russian dolphin coins

Thai coin ring

Hoe-shaped coin

Early American coins

Chinese round coin with square hole for stringing

Chinese knife-shaped coin

Earliest coin, issued by the King of Lydia

Kenyan hundred-shilling note

Japanese feudal note

Many people see a tiny white owl or spider in the upper right corner of each one-dollar bill.

## Paper Money

Although it was handier to carry a pocketful of coins than commodity money, metal money didn't work as well when you had to buy big items that cost a lot. Large sacks of money were too heavy, too bulky, and too easy to steal.

Paper money was first used in China during the 600s. As its use gradually spread all over the world, governments became involved in printing money, each one printing its own type. The United States has had printed money since 1781.

Paper money has value only when a government declares that people must accept it as payment for things. Bills may be the same size, but have different values according to what is printed on them.

*Two Roses on a Tablecloth* by the 19th-century painter Édouard Manet.

# The Act

There were the roses, in the rain.
Don't cut them, I pleaded.
They won't last, she said
But they're so beautiful
where they are.
Agh, we were all beautiful once, she said,
and cut them and gave them to me
in my hand.

William Carlos Williams

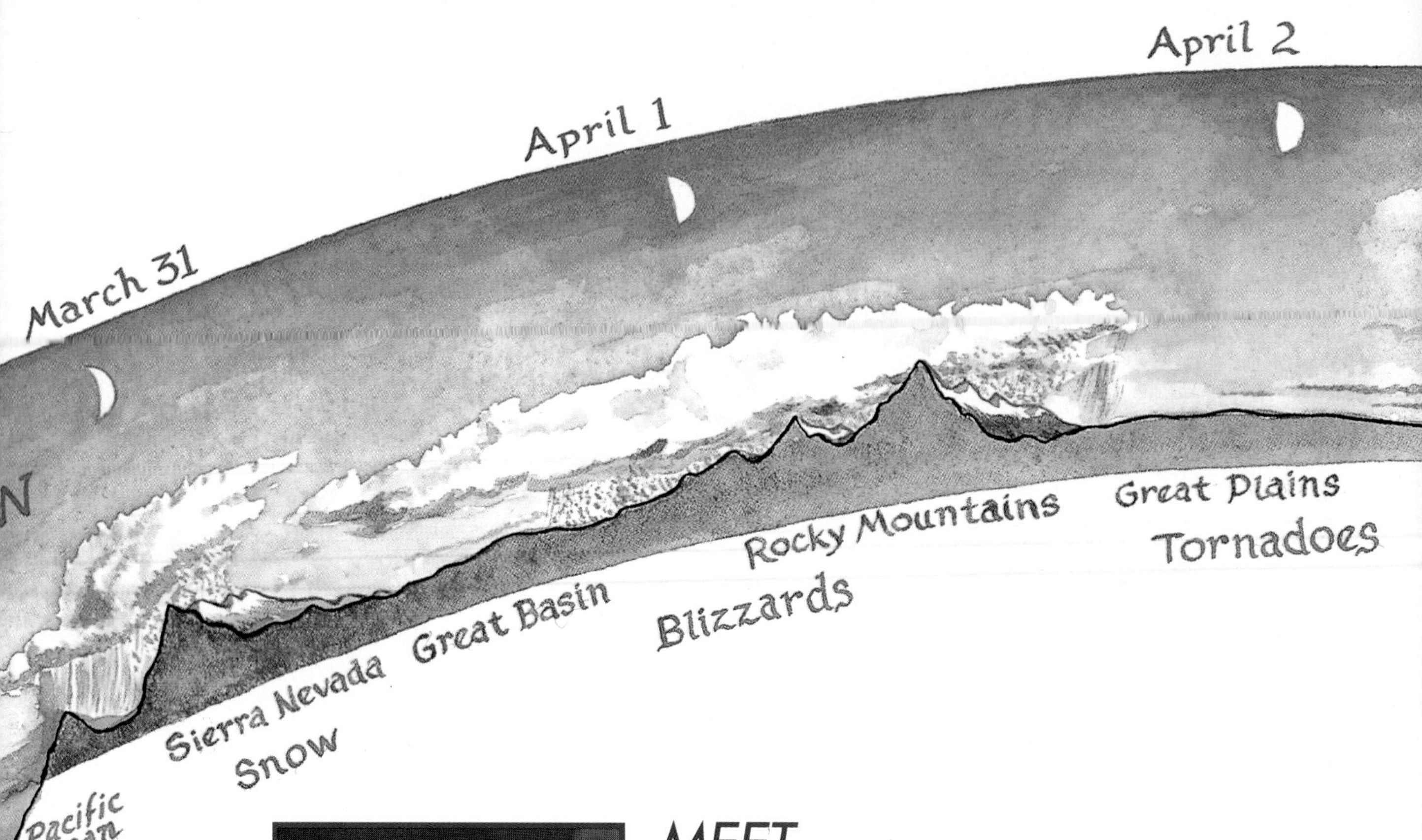

# MEET BRUCE HISCOCK

Bruce Hiscock began work on *The Big Storm* by calling up weather reporters from the radio. "I had them suggest storms to write about. I wanted a spring storm because they are the most violent and active." Hiscock then studied weather for six months. He felt he had to learn all he could about weather to understand this storm fully. For details, Hiscock read newspaper accounts from towns hit by the storm. He also visited places pictured in his book.

From his cabin in the Adirondack Mountains, Hiscock stays in touch with nature. "I spend time every day in the woods with the birds and the animals. At night I watch the stars with a telescope. . . ." A billion-year-old boulder near his home is the subject of another Hiscock book, *The Big Rock*.

# THE BIG STORM

written and illustrated by Bruce Hiscock

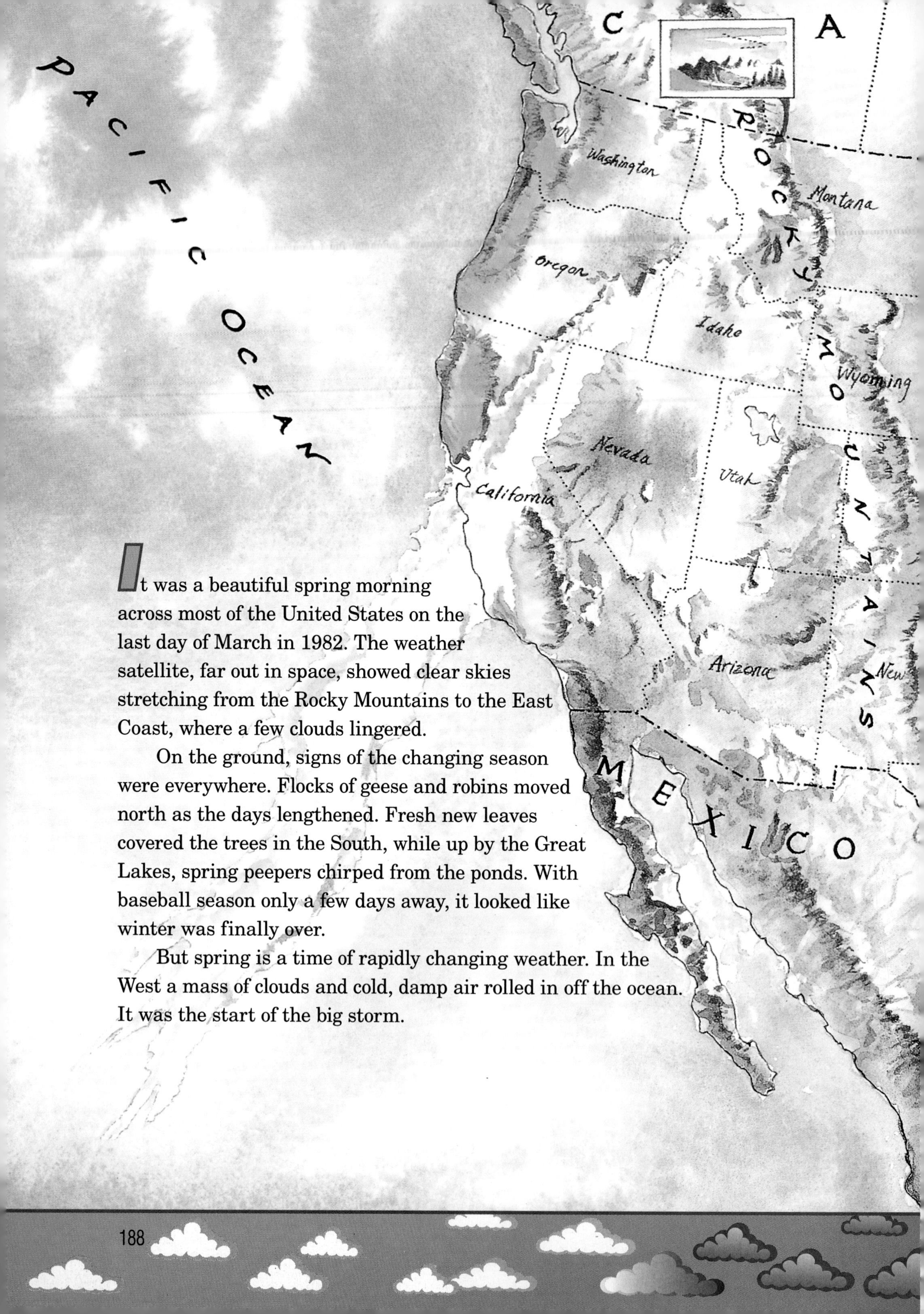


It was a beautiful spring morning across most of the United States on the last day of March in 1982. The weather satellite, far out in space, showed clear skies stretching from the Rocky Mountains to the East Coast, where a few clouds lingered.

On the ground, signs of the changing season were everywhere. Flocks of geese and robins moved north as the days lengthened. Fresh new leaves covered the trees in the South, while up by the Great Lakes, spring peepers chirped from the ponds. With baseball season only a few days away, it looked like winter was finally over.

But spring is a time of rapidly changing weather. In the West a mass of clouds and cold, damp air rolled in off the ocean. It was the start of the big storm.

N A D A
GREAT PLAINS
North Dakota
South Dakota
Nebraska
Kansas
Oklahoma
Texas
Colorado
Minnesota
Iowa
Missouri
Arkansas
Louisiana
Wisconsin
Illinois
Mississippi
Michigan
GREAT LAKES
Indiana
Ohio
Kentucky
Tennessee
Alabama
Georgia
Florida
West Virginia
Virginia
North Carolina
South Carolina
Pennsylvania
New York
New Jersey
Del.
Massachusetts
Connecticut
R.I.
Vermont
New Hampshire
Maine
ATLANTIC OCEAN
CUBA

The clouds brought heavy rain to the Pacific Coast as the gathering storm moved inland. Like most weather systems in North America, it was carried along by the westerlies, the winds that nearly always blow from west to east across the continent.

When the storm ran up against the mountains of the Sierra Nevada range in California, the wind pushed the clouds up the steep slopes. In the cold mountain air the rain changed to snow.

It snowed hard all day in the Sierras. The flakes clung to the tall pines, coating them in heavy layers of white. But near the mountaintops, where no trees grow, the wind piled the snow into great drifts. Soon the drifts became so deep that the slopes would hold no more.

The snow began to slide from the high places, gently at first, then faster and faster, until the slides became huge avalanches. The avalanches roared down the mountains and slammed into buildings. Several people were killed.

Any storm can be dangerous as well as beautiful, but this one was a real powerhouse. And it was just getting started.

The storm moved swiftly over the Rocky Mountains, spreading blizzards from Montana to Arizona. In Colorado fierce winds gusted to 141 miles per hour, overturning vans and campers. In Nebraska the wind blew hard enough to move cow chips around.

The strongest winds came right at the leading edge of the storm. There a cold front marked the boundary between the warm springlike air covering most of the country and the cold, stormy air rushing in. Big masses of warm and cold air do not mix when they meet but instead push each other around. The line where the air masses bump is called a front.

This front was a cold front because the cold air was pushing the warm air away. Strong cold fronts usually bring high winds and sometimes violent weather.

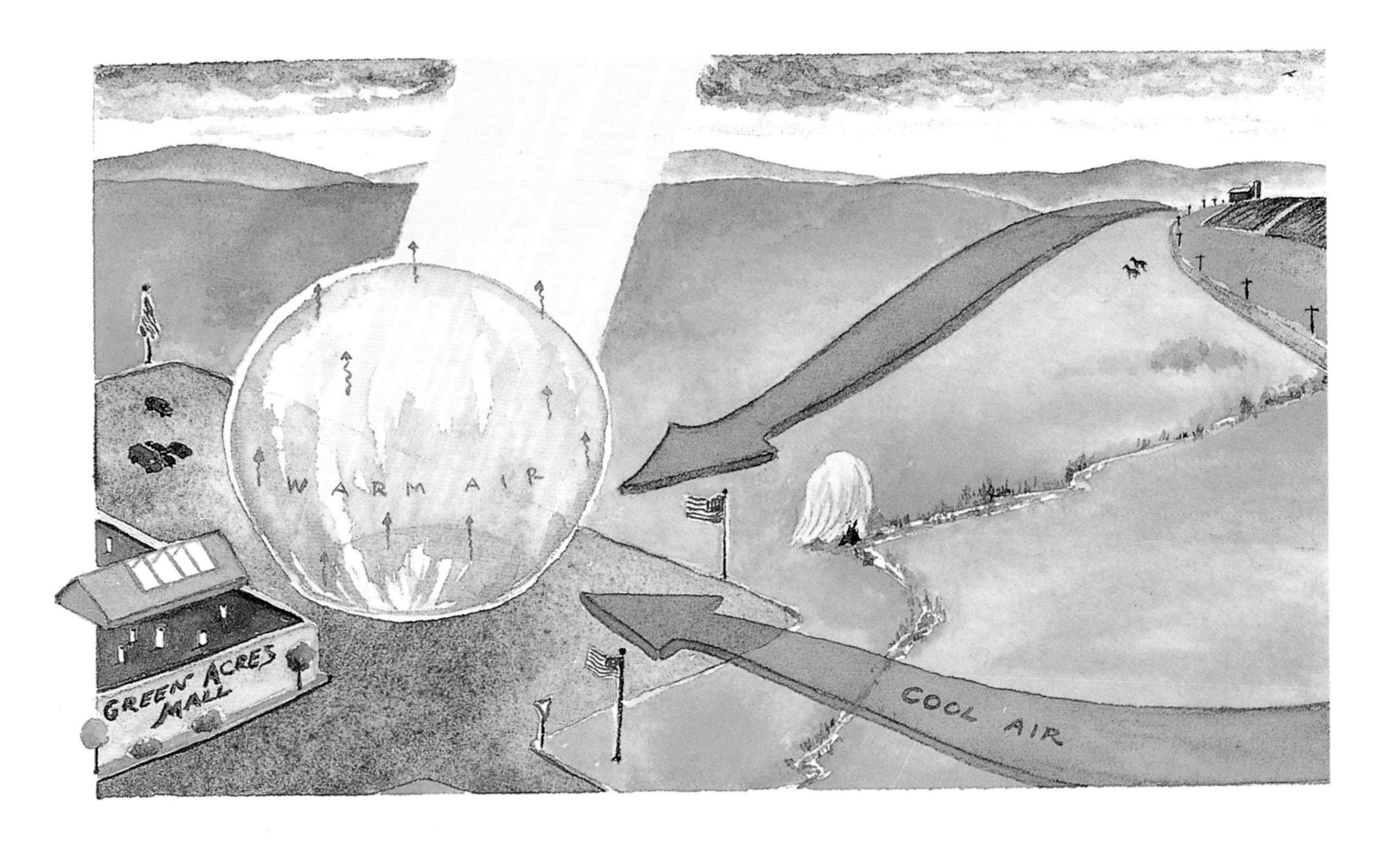


The tremendous power of weather comes from the sun. Our planet is surrounded by a thin layer of air called the atmosphere, which is a mixture of gases, clouds, and dust. Heat from the sun causes the atmosphere to flow and swirl around the earth.

For instance, imagine that your city or county is covered by a blanket of cool, cloudy air. No wind stirs the leaves, and temperatures are the same everywhere.

Now let the clouds open slightly so that sunlight falls on a plowed field or a parking lot at the mall. The sun warms the earth or the pavement, which in turn heats the air right above it. Hot air rises, and soon a huge bubble of warm air is going up like an invisible balloon.

As the warm air rises, cool air flows in along the ground to take its place, causing a breeze. Temperatures begin to change. The sun has made the atmosphere move.

The same sort of uneven heating keeps the atmosphere moving worldwide. Warm air rises from the tropics while cold air flows down from the poles. This heating pattern and others create the vast wind and weather systems of the planet. Of course, these weather systems change with the seasons. The long summer days provide much more sunlight to warm and lift the air than the short, cold days of winter.

The sun moves the weather, but the land and sea affect it too. Ocean currents cool or warm the air. Hills and mountains block the wind. Even the spinning of the earth changes the wind's direction.

In fact, so many things affect the weather that when a storm comes up, it is not easy to predict exactly what it will do.

The big storm grew worse as it swept out over the Great Plains. Flocks of robins huddled on the ground, unable to fly in the blowing snow. Across the Dakotas and Minnesota, weather forecasters watched their barometers as the readings fell to record low levels. A deep low-pressure center was forming.

Barometers measure the pressure of the air directly overhead. Air, like water, has weight, and tons of air press down on the earth. This force, called barometric or atmospheric pressure, changes constantly as the air moves.

Forecasters pay close attention to these changes, for they help predict the weather to come. High pressure usually brings fair skies. Low pressure means storms, and the lower the pressure, the stronger the storm.

As the blizzard raged on, the weather stations in the storm reported the low pressure, the freezing temperatures, and the gusty wind and snow conditions to the National Meteorological Center near Washington, D.C. The data went directly into their huge computers along with data from hundreds of other weather stations, satellites, and instrument-carrying balloons.

The computer gave an overall picture of the weather to the forecasters at the National Center. Then, using more computers, they predicted what the storm would do next. These predictions were sent back to each weather station. There, a detailed forecast was made for the local area.

This work goes on every day, but with a killer storm on the loose, the forecasts were especially important.

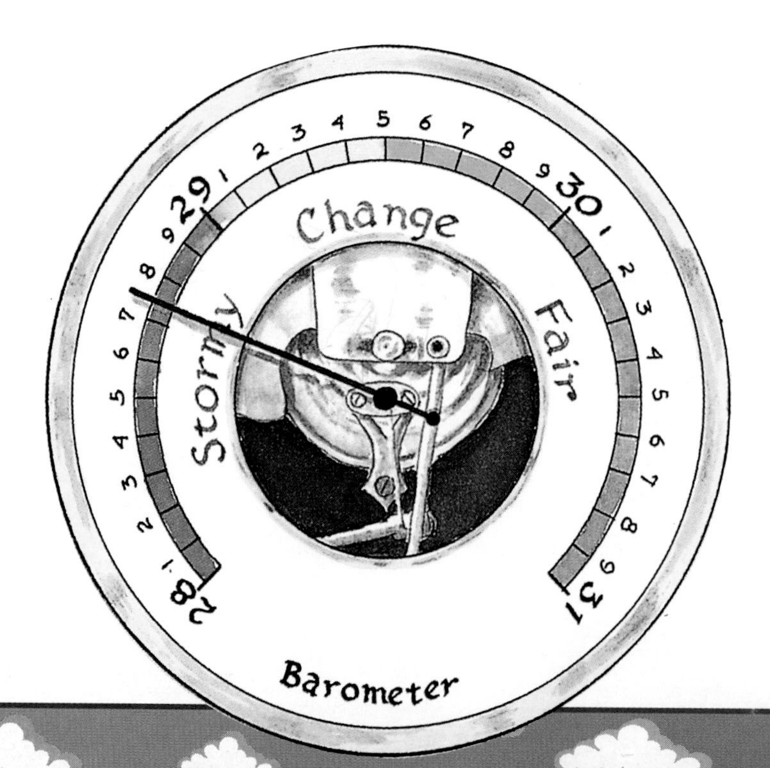

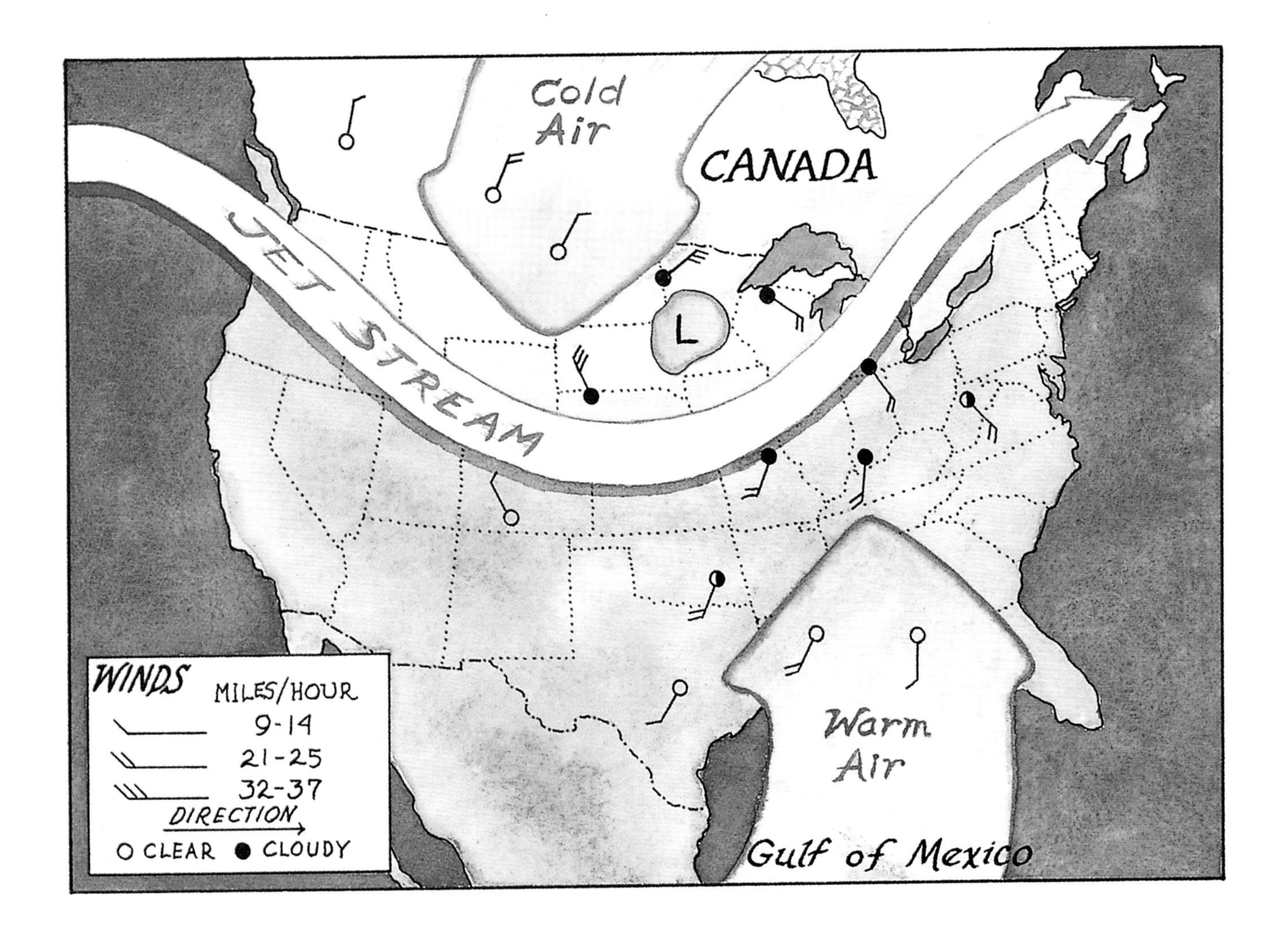


On the morning of Friday, April 2, the weather map showed strong surface winds blowing in toward the low-pressure center. Areas of low pressure push enormous amounts of air upward, causing air near the ground to rush in from all sides, like air rushing into a vacuum cleaner. Far above the surface, the jet stream, a narrow band of high-speed wind that snakes across the continent, formed a giant curve around the low.

All this was creating a huge counterclockwise swirl in the atmosphere typical of big storms. On one side of the swirl warm, moist air from the Gulf of Mexico was being drawn north. On the backside, frigid air was coming down out of Canada.

The National Severe Storm Forecast Center in Kansas City, Missouri, began plotting where these two air masses would meet. Chances were good that the collision would result in a powerful cold front, producing violent thunderstorms and tornadoes.

Local weather stations from Texas to Iowa and east were alerted. A Severe Weather Watch was announced on radio and television to warn that bad weather was possible. Forecasters checked their radar screens constantly, looking for signs of the front. Everyone waited.

The afternoon was warm and humid when a line of towering clouds appeared across the Texas plains. Lightning flashed in the distance. Soon the rumble of thunder was heard. Airports closed. Dogs whined and hid under beds. The clouds came on, churning and billowing. An eerie darkness fell. Then slashing winds hit. Rain and hail poured down. The cold front raced through. Temperatures dropped sharply.

All along the front, police and other spotters watched for tornadoes. Tornadoes are violent whirlwinds, funnel-shaped clouds that may spiral down from thunderstorms. They are extremely dangerous. The spotters watched anxiously, for they knew that weather radar can pinpoint thunderstorms but usually cannot "see" tornadoes. Eyes are better for that.

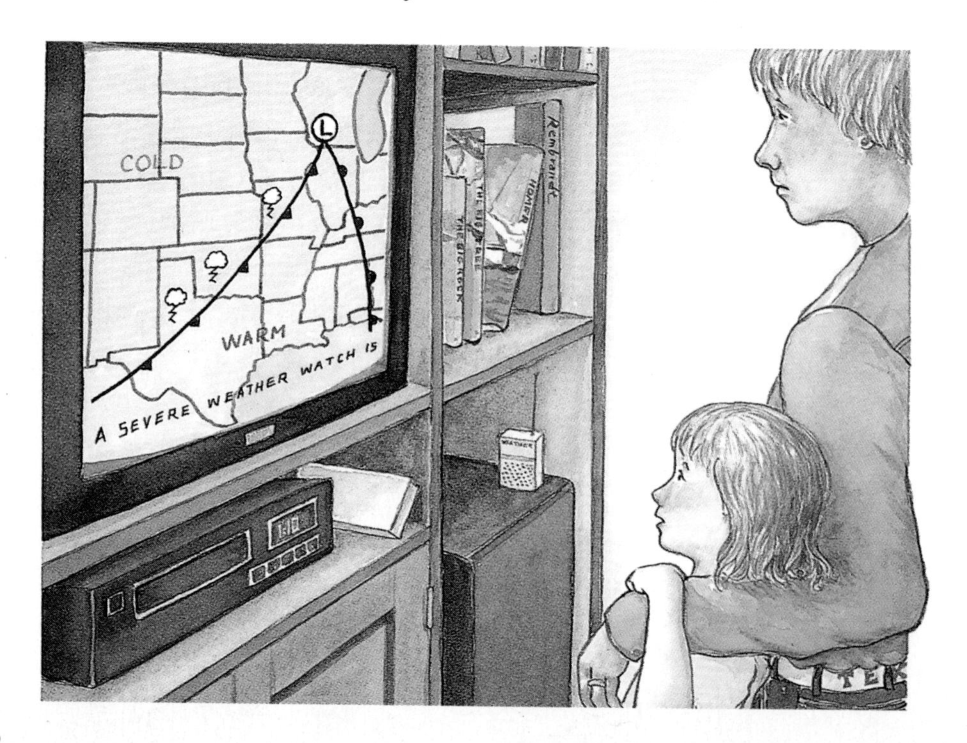

Suddenly a tornado was sighted heading for Paris, Texas. Sirens blew. A Tornado Warning was broadcast. Families rushed for the nearest bathroom, closet, or basement shelter.

The tornado hit with the roar of a freight train. Houses and churches were torn apart. Trees shattered. Cars were tossed around.

The funnel cloud stayed down for twenty minutes, ripping a path through the city two blocks wide and five miles long. Most of the people in the path survived, though many were injured. Ten people were killed.

More than eighty tornadoes touched down that afternoon and night in Texas, Oklahoma, Arkansas, Missouri, and other states as far east as Ohio. Even with the warning broadcasts, over thirty people died, and the damage was horrendous. The United States has more tornadoes than anyplace else in the world, but this was the worst outbreak since 1974.

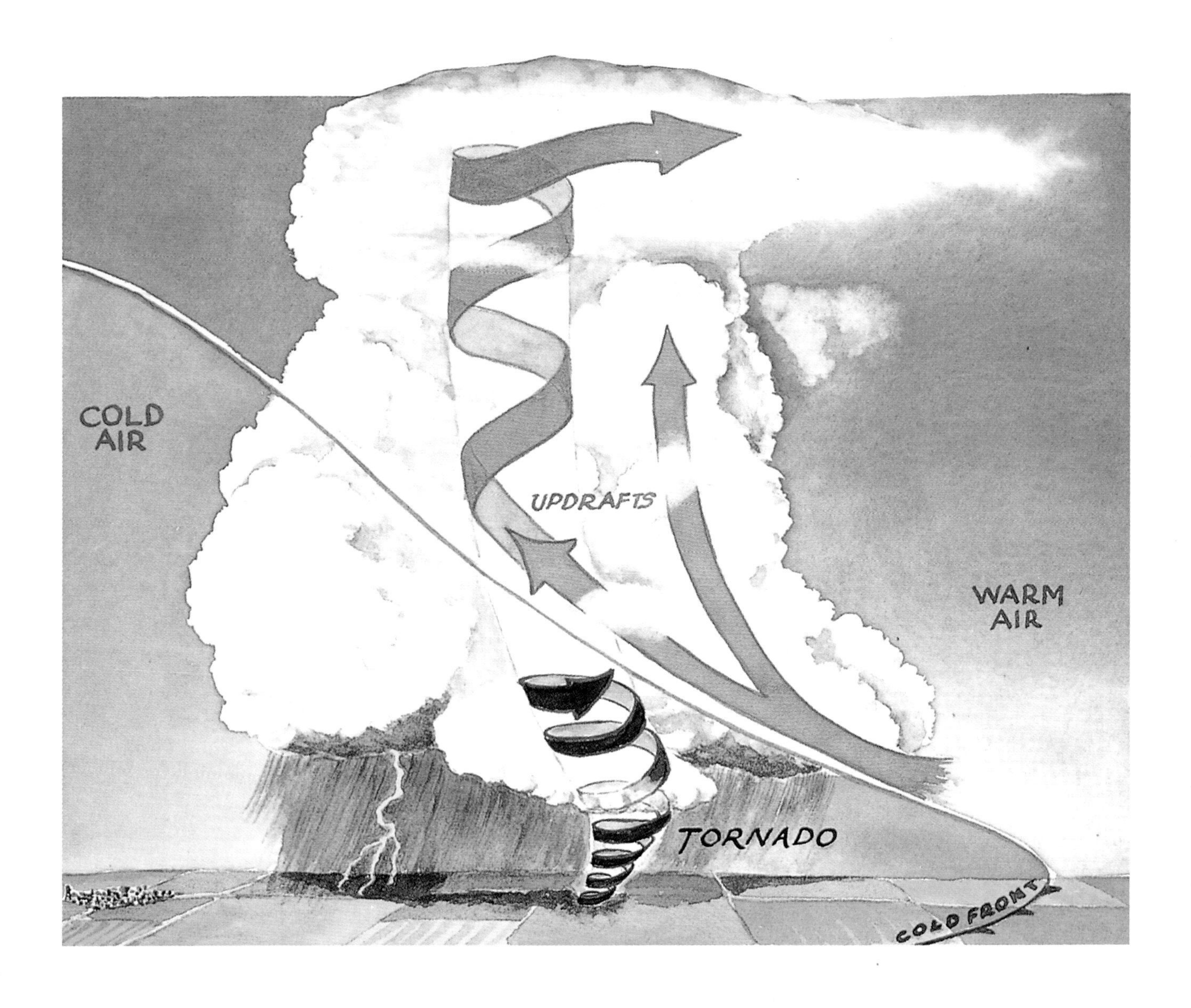


Tornadoes usually form just behind a cold front as the wedge of cold, dense air pushes in, forcing the warm, moist air to rise very quickly. This produces strong updraft winds and huge thunderclouds.

If an updraft begins to spin, it may set off a tornado. Exactly what causes the spinning is not completely understood, but once the twister is formed, it sucks in air, dirt, and anything else it touches with winds of over two hundred miles an hour. Boards, bricks, and glass become deadly flying missiles. Huge funnel clouds can even lift railroad cars.

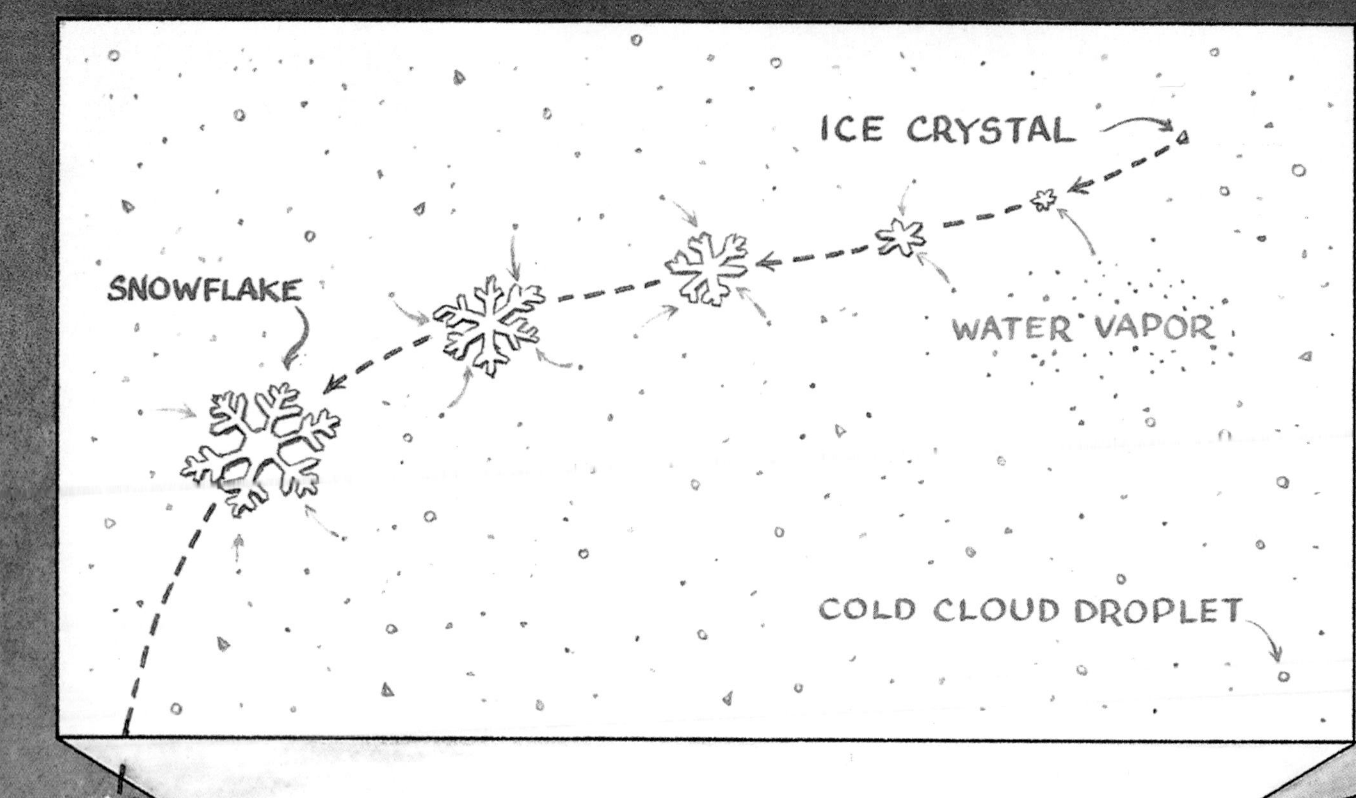


When the front passed, the tornadoes stopped, but thunderstorms continued throughout the South. Heavy rain drenched Alabama and Georgia. Hail the size of golf balls dented cars and broke windows in Kentucky.

Rain and hail are formed from the moisture in clouds, but they are not simply falling bits of mist and ice. The water droplets and tiny ice crystals that make up clouds are far too small to fall by themselves, and so they remain suspended in air like fog.

Surprisingly, most raindrops start out as snowflakes. High in the cloud where the air is very cold, ice crystals gradually grow into snowflakes that are heavy enough to fall. The snowflakes then melt, if it is warm near the ground, and become raindrops. A raindrop is about a million times larger than a cloud droplet.

RAINDROP

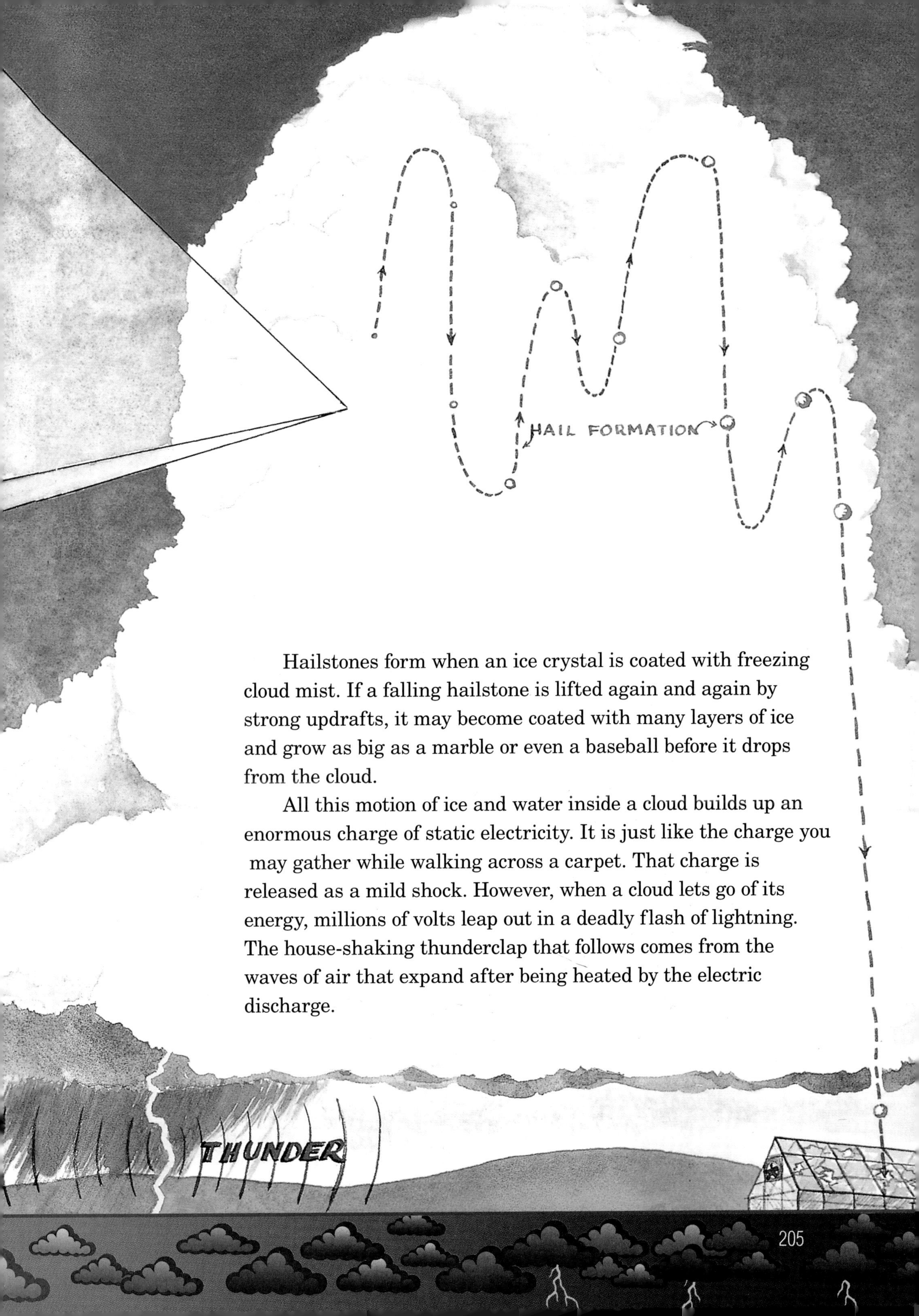


Hailstones form when an ice crystal is coated with freezing cloud mist. If a falling hailstone is lifted again and again by strong updrafts, it may become coated with many layers of ice and grow as big as a marble or even a baseball before it drops from the cloud.

All this motion of ice and water inside a cloud builds up an enormous charge of static electricity. It is just like the charge you may gather while walking across a carpet. That charge is released as a mild shock. However, when a cloud lets go of its energy, millions of volts leap out in a deadly flash of lightning. The house-shaking thunderclap that follows comes from the waves of air that expand after being heated by the electric discharge.

For the next three days the huge mass of Arctic air behind the cold front brought more snow and high winds to the Midwest. Driving became very dangerous. Five hundred travelers were stranded in Michigan and had to spend the night in school gyms. Rush-hour traffic in Chicago was a tangle of accidents.

The great swirl of clouds around the low was clearly visible from space, and as the swirl drifted east, clear skies and intense cold followed it. With no blanket of clouds at night, the earth rapidly lost heat to outer space. Low temperature records were set from Idaho to the Appalachians. And still the storm was not through!

Tuesday, April 6, was opening day for the baseball season, and the New York Yankees were scheduled to play at home. The main storm center was now out at sea, but still the forecast was not good. Cold air continued to pour in, forming new lows over Pennsylvania and the New Jersey coast.

Around three in the morning, snow began to fall softly on New York City. In the Northeast the great snowstorms often begin very quietly. Soon the wind picked up. By noon it was a howling blizzard. Traffic snarled. Trains were delayed. The pace of the great city slowed to a sloppy walk.

Over a foot of snow fell in New York before the storm moved on to Boston. It was the first blizzard ever to hit New York City in April. The Yankee game was delayed for four days. Many adults said bad things about the weather, but few kids complained. They all had a day off from school.

The big storm finally ended. Snow turned to slush and melted away. People cleaned up their towns. Spring returned. Birds began traveling north again, and the evenings lost their chill.

The storm is just a memory now, but every spring the cycle repeats itself. Warm air from the south meets with cold Arctic air, triggering storms of all sizes and giving the United States one of the most varied and exciting climates on earth.

# Change

The summer
still hangs
heavy and sweet
with sunlight
as it did last year.

The autumn
still comes
showering gold and crimson
as it did last year.

The winter
still stings
clean and cold and white
as it did last year.

The spring
still comes
like a whisper in the dark night.

It is only I
who have changed.

Charlotte Zolotow

CHARTS AND TABLES

# People Who Like to Build

| WORKER | PART OF BUILDING |
|---|---|
| **Architect** | Entire building |
| **Carpenter** | Entire building |
| **Construction Supervisor** | Entire building |
| **Developer** | Entire building |
| **Estimator** | Entire building |
| **Expeditor** | Entire building |
| **Plumber** | Entire building |
| **Stonemason** | Outside of building |

**It takes many people to construct a building or to renovate an old one. Maybe a career in building is something you'd like to try. This is only a handful of the many job opportunities available in the building profession.**

| WORKER'S ROLE | EDUCATION | ENVIRONMENT |
|---|---|---|
| Designs and plans building to be built and renovated | College degree; graduate work | Office and construction site; mostly indoors |
| Works with wood to construct building and its parts | High school not mandatory; must be 17 years old to join 4-year apprentice program | Construction site; indoors and outdoors |
| Manages and oversees crew at the construction site | High school diploma; extensive on-the-job construction experience | Construction site; indoors and outdoors |
| Obtains and provides money for project; schedules and manages all operations | High school diploma; extensive management experience | Office and construction site; mostly indoors |
| Figures out how much building will cost to build | High school diploma; technical or junior college training available | Office and construction site; mostly indoors |
| Buys building materials | High school diploma; technical or junior college training available | Office and wholesalers' offices; mostly indoors |
| Assembles and installs pipe systems to carry water | High school diploma recommended; 4–5 years apprenticeship | Office and construction site; mostly indoors |
| Works with stone to create outside of building | High school not mandatory; technical or junior college training available | Office and construction site; mostly outdoors |

## COINS OF THE OLD WORLD

GREEK DECADRACHM
(5th century B.C.)

SPANISH PIECES OF EIGHT

ITALIAN TESTONE
(16th century)

ROMAN DENARIUS
(1st century A.D.)

JUDEAN
WIDOW'S MITE
(1st century A.D.)

ISLAMIC FATIMID
(11th century)

ENGLISH PENNY
(14th century)

BYZANTINE NOMISMA

VENETIAN DUCAT
(13th century)

**coin** (koin), a stamped or embossed disk that is generally made of metal and used as money. Coins are necessary for completing small, everyday financial transactions, and the minting of them is an important function of national governments. Unlike paper currency, which merely represents value, coins have a value in themselves.

Most modern coins bear designs and words that are impressed into the surface of the coin during minting. In the typical minting operation the metal to be used is melted and cast into bars. The bars are divided into coin strips of regulated thickness. The strips are fed to a cutting machine, where carbon-steel dies punch out blank coins. The coins are then milled by a machine that raises their edges above the surface. This process makes it easier to stack the coins and also minimizes surface wear. Finally, the coins are fed to a hydraulic press that imprints symbols and words under tremendous pressure. At the same time the rims of the more valuable coins receive a pattern of indentations to prevent people from shaving off bits of the metal.

### History

In early civilizations, goods were acquired by barter, or the direct exchange of one commodity for another. When coins became the principal medium of exchange, such metals as gold, silver, bronze, copper, lead, and iron were used to mint them. The first known coins were introduced in Lydia in Asia Minor and in China about the 8th century B.C. The Lydian coins, probably issued by private rather than by state sources, were made of a natural alloy of gold and silver, known as electrum. Governments soon assumed the responsibility for authorizing and producing coins. By the end of the 6th century B.C., gold and silver coins were being minted in many Greek city-states. As Athens became the commercial center of the Aegean Sea area, its coins were used and imitated throughout the region.

The first Roman coins were made of bronze, and they date from about the 4th century B.C. Gold and silver were used during the period of the later Roman Empire. After the fall of Rome in the 5th century A.D., Byzantine and Merovingian gold coins and, later, Carolingian silver coins were used extensively in European trade centers. With the breaking up of the Carolingian Empire various cities and states made their own coins, which were mostly crude thin silver pieces. As Genoa and Venice rose in commercial importance in the 12th century, Italian coins became the predominant medium of exchange.

The early American colonists used Indian wampum as money. Wampum consisted of small shell beads made into belts. The value of wampum was not based on the worth of its material as much as on the labor required to produce the belts. In the colonial period European coins were circulated in America, but their value fluctuated from colony to colony and from one locality to another. In 1652 the Massachusetts Bay colony produced the first coins minted in America. During the American Revolution the Continental Congress issued coins made of pewter, silver, and brass.

The U.S. Mint was established in Philadelphia in 1792, and its first coins were circulated the following year. In the American Civil War the Confederacy printed paper money because of the shortage of metal to make coins. After the war, bank notes, checks, drafts, and other forms of paper currency increased in use, while metal currency continued to decline. In 1933 the United States discontinued entirely the use of gold coins in domestic and foreign commerce. It is still legal, however, for coin collectors to save them and to exchange them with other collectors.

## AMERICAN COINS OF THE PAST
(Both sides of each coin are shown.)

PINE TREE SHILLING

FUGIO CENT

CONFEDERATE HALF-DOLLAR

COMMEMORATIVE ISABELLA QUARTER

$20 GOLD PIECE

Coins have always reflected the degree of prosperity enjoyed by the nations issuing them. The Romans often devaluated their coins to pay their debts with "cheap" money during financial crises. Similar depreciation of coins was common at various times in all later European states. It occurred whenever rulers resorted to reminting coins at a reduced ratio of gold and silver to make up for the lack of available funds. In more modern times the silver content of British coins was decreased with the decline of the British Empire after World War I. By 1947 British "silver" coins had lost all their silver content and were being made of a mixture of copper and nickel, called cupronickel.

### Coin Design

The earliest coins were seldom imprinted with words, but most of them bore symbols on both their observe, or front and reverse, back sides. Generally, the designs represented animals, religious subjects, military heroes, or civil authorities. The head of the goddess Athena was frequently depicted on Athenian coins. Roman coins commemorated great victories or bore a representation of the head of an emperor or of a god. Many ancient coins are outstanding for their artistic qualities. Syracuse, a trade center in Sicily, produced some of the most beautiful coins, and certain of its skilled craftsmen and artists have become known to generations through the coins they designed.

Through the ages the coins of all countries typically have carried the profile of a present or past chief of state and a motto. Many U.S. coins bear a representation of the head of a former President. The date of issue and the denomination appear on all U.S. coins, and almost all coins bear such inscriptions as "Liberty," "In God We Trust," and "*E Pluribus Unum*," a Latin phrase meaning "one from many."

### Coin Collecting

There are an estimated 400,000 numismatists, or coin collectors, in the United States. The prime consideration in determining the worth of a coin is supply and demand. The condition of a coin also affects its value. A coin that shows little or no surface wear is far more valuable than another of the same year that shows signs of considerable handling or wear. Ancient coins are often valuable regardless of condition.

In large collections, coins are usually wrapped individually and kept in trays stored in metal cabinets. Smaller collections and display pieces are kept in specially designed albums and folders. Many albums include cutout spaces for inserting a series of related coins. An important part of collecting is the ability to recognize counterfeit coins. Counterfeits usually make a dull sound when they are dropped on a hard surface, and many of them feel greasy. They also have irregular edges, and some of them can be easily cut with a knife. Many numismatists collect only the coins of a specific country, and some collect coins regardless of origin. Other collectors specialize in tokens, commemorative medals, and paper money in addition to the coins of one or more countries.

Books for Further Study

*How to Build a Coin Collection* by Fred Reinfeld and Burton H. Hobson (Sterling, 1977).

*The Coin Atlas: The World of Coinage from Its Origins to the Present Day* by Joe Cribb and others (Facts on File, 1990).

*Collecting Coins for Pleasure & Profit: A Comprehensive Guide and Handbook for Collectors and Investors* by Barry Krause (Betterway Publications, 1991).

*Standard Catalog of World Coins* by Chester L. Krause and Clifford Mishler (Krause, published annually).

# MAPS

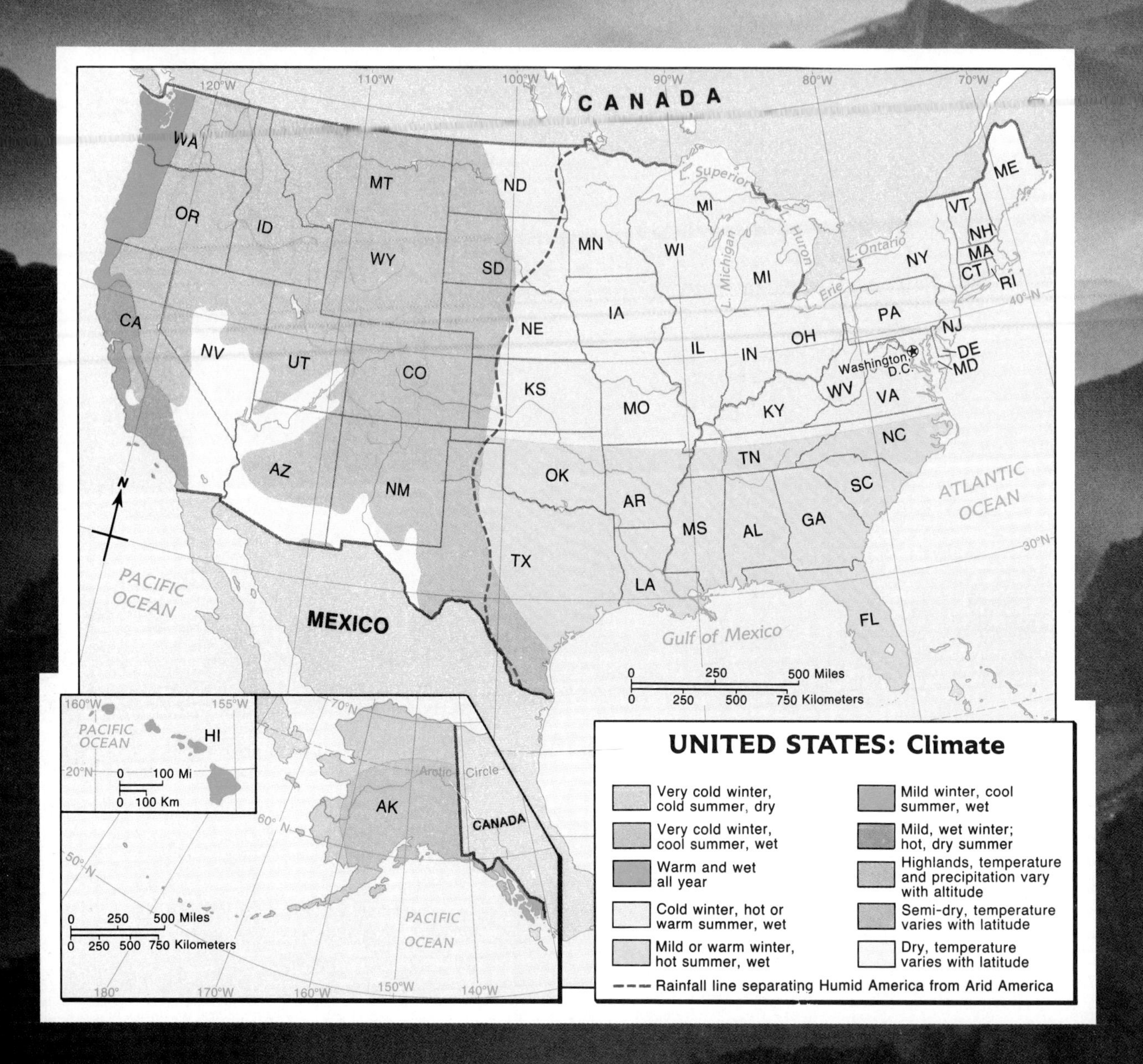

UNITED STATES: Climate
CANADA
MEXICO
PACIFIC OCEAN
ATLANTIC OCEAN
Gulf of Mexico
L. Superior
L. Michigan
L. Huron
L. Erie
L. Ontario
WA
OR
CA
ID
NV
MT
WY
UT
AZ
CO
NM
ND
SD
NE
KS
OK
TX
MN
IA
MO
AR
LA
WI
IL
MI
IN
OH
KY
TN
MS
AL
GA
FL
SC
NC
VA
WV
PA
NY
NJ
DE
MD
Washington, D.C.
VT
NH
MA
CT
RI
ME
HI
AK
Arctic Circle
120°W
110°W
100°W
90°W
80°W
70°W
40°N
30°N
160°W
155°W
20°N
60°N
50°N
180°
170°W
150°W
140°W
N
0 250 500 Miles
0 250 500 750 Kilometers
0 100 Mi
0 100 Km
Very cold winter, cold summer, dry
Very cold winter, cool summer, wet
Warm and wet all year
Cold winter, hot or warm summer, wet
Mild or warm winter, hot summer, wet
Mild winter, cool summer, wet
Mild, wet winter; hot, dry summer
Highlands, temperature and precipitation vary with altitude
Semi-dry, temperature varies with latitude
Dry, temperature varies with latitude
Rainfall line separating Humid America from Arid America

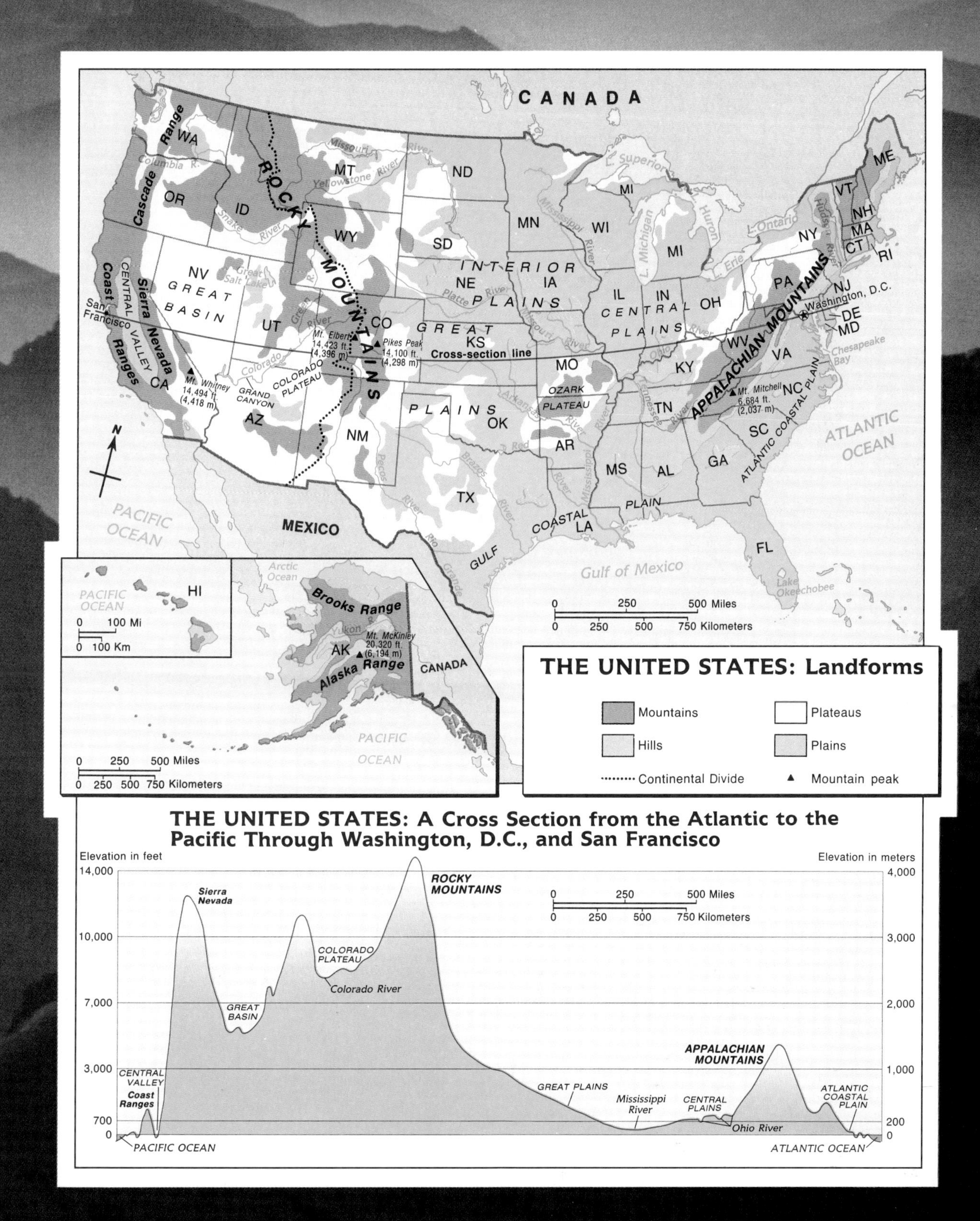
THE UNITED STATES: Landforms
Mountains
Plateaus
Hills
Plains
Continental Divide
Mountain peak
CANADA
MEXICO
PACIFIC OCEAN
ATLANTIC OCEAN
Gulf of Mexico
ROCKY MOUNTAINS
APPALACHIAN MOUNTAINS
INTERIOR PLAINS
GREAT PLAINS
CENTRAL PLAINS
GREAT BASIN
COLORADO PLATEAU
OZARK PLATEAU
GULF COASTAL PLAIN
ATLANTIC COASTAL PLAIN
Cascade Range
Sierra Nevada
Coast Ranges
CENTRAL VALLEY
GRAND CANYON
Mt. Whitney 14,494 ft. (4,418 m)
Mt. Elbert 14,423 ft. (4,396 m)
Pikes Peak 14,100 ft. (4,298 m)
Mt. Mitchell 6,684 ft. (2,037 m)
Cross-section line
Washington, D.C.
San Francisco
Brooks Range
Alaska Range
Mt. McKinley 20,320 ft. (6,194 m)
0 250 500 Miles
0 250 500 750 Kilometers
0 100 Mi
0 100 Km
THE UNITED STATES: A Cross Section from the Atlantic to the Pacific Through Washington, D.C., and San Francisco
Elevation in feet
Elevation in meters
14,000
10,000
7,000
3,000
700
0
4,000
3,000
2,000
1,000
200
PACIFIC OCEAN
ATLANTIC OCEAN
Coast Ranges
Sierra Nevada
GREAT BASIN
COLORADO PLATEAU
Colorado River
ROCKY MOUNTAINS
GREAT PLAINS
Mississippi River
CENTRAL PLAINS
Ohio River
APPALACHIAN MOUNTAINS
ATLANTIC COASTAL PLAIN

Headline

Byline

# The Blue and Gold

Spring 1996 | The Warbleton School Newspaper | Hunterville, California

## Omar Sanchez To Receive Special Award

**by Judy Cator**
*Student Reporter*

This year Warbleton leads city-wide when it comes to one student who cares about the community. The Hunterville Chamber of Commerce will honor a Warbleton fifth-grader for helping to launch a new city program to recycle plastic toys. His name is Omar Sanchez.

The recycling program, which may be the only community operation in the country that deals with toys, is now in full effect throughout Hunterville. However, it never would have come to pass if Omar had not become concerned about the problem of plastic waste. "I began noticing a lot of toys in the garbage around my neighborhood," he said. "As soon as they break or their owner outgrows them, they get tossed."

Omar's awareness of the problem came from a class project on recycling. For the project he had prepared a report on the ways in which plastics, paper, glass, and aluminum products are recycled and reused to make new products. After writing to the Departments of Sanitation of several cities, he discovered that recycling efforts differ from city to city and town to town.

Omar decided to look into our town's recycling program to see how effective it really is. For over 3 months he kept track of several trash cans in several different neighborhoods. He listed the different kinds of plastic, metal, glass, or paper being thrown away, and kept note of which of these were being recycled. He found out that plastic toys made up a significant portion of trash that could be recycled. The only problem was that Hunterville had no laws requiring the recycling of plastic toys.

It took 3 more months of gathering statistics, several letters to the town council, and the support of prominent adults in the city for Omar's plan to go into effect. The town council had to form a special committee to investigate the costs of recycling plastic toys. Although some were made from the same kind of plastic as food containers already being recycled, other kinds of toy plastic required special processing.

When the problems about recycling toys were revealed, 6 council members spoke out against the project, saying it would be too costly. That's when Omar went back to work. With the help of his father, who is a chemist at Bradley Labs, he helped create a proposal that would lower the budget on recycling toys and presented it by himself to the Council.

It was finally decided that toys for recycling could be sorted in Hunterville, but that a part of them would be shipped to a plant in nearby Mill Creek on a weekly basis. The new plan will cost taxpayers some money. An additional $48,000 will be needed to add plastic toys to the list of recyclable products.

"I think the extra cost is worth it," said Omar. "Recycling toys will teach the kids who play with them to think about what making them costs us and the environment. It might make the cost of the toys lower as well."

Omar will be honored by a special dinner and award ceremony on April 23. We at Warbleton are planning to honor him as well. On May 15 a special assembly hosted by our student officers will be held in the auditorium. There, Omar will explain how he developed his plan for recycling toys.

Way to go, Omar!

## *Maypole Day Will be a Spring "Riot"*

**By Bobby Santiago**

Letisha Foster and Billie Schwartz, who head the Maypole Day planning committee, are promising to make this year's Maypole Day celebrations even "wilder" than last year's. Those of you who came to last year's party in the rear playground probably remember the good times had by all. There were one-legged races, a students vs. teachers touch-football game, and an open-air barbecue. But this year, Letisha and Billie say they will add disco to the mix.

There will be seven student D.J.'s, picked by Letisha Foster, Billie Schwartz, and the rest of the Maypole Day planning committee. The committee is taking applications now. There will also be a team of teacher judges to give awards to the best dancers in hip hop, free-style, and line dancing.

As if all this were not enough, Barnaby's Fabrics has donated 600 inches of surplus ribbon for the Maypole Dance. Over 70 ribbons of different colors will be hung from the flag pole. We'll wind them around it to the accordion music of Susan Hammond, a Warbleton fifth-grader.

Volunteer barbecue chef-assistants, servers, and clean-up people are needed for this event. So if you're interested, sign up in Ms. Hardy's room between 8:00 A.M. and 3:00 P.M. any day this week.

See you there!

**CONTENTS**

## In My Opinion

Editorial

### *Let's Help Out*

As the editors of The Blue and Gold we feel that students at Warbleton School should get involved in the community. Omar Sanchez did a great job setting up a recycling project and should be an example for all of us. But don't think that to make a difference you have to do something as ambitious as Omar Sanchez's project. There are a lot of fun ways to get involved.

A great way is to help out at the The Huntsville Senior Center, behind the school on Oak Drive. Many Senior Citizens helped us out at the Winter Carnival last month, and now they need help organizing and setting up their annual Crafts Fair. They need people to set up and decorate the auditorium the week before the Fair. On Saturday and Sunday they need help selling food and drinks and cleaning up afterwards.

They were a great help to us last month, so let's return the favor and lend a hand with the Crafts Fair in a few weeks. The Center needs volunteers year round too, as many residents don't have families in the area and want someone to spend time with them a few days a week. You can help them write letters, play a game, go for a walk, or just talk. Sign up on the activities board to help, and get involved!

## *The Blue and Gold* CLASSIFIEDS

**TO SELL**

Antique Comic Collection. Mint Condition. Over 200 comics going back to 1949. Singles, series, or entire collection. Price negotiable. Call Marcy at 555-8989.

Miniature Railroad. Full set, only slightly used. Bought for $239 new. Your price: $110. Bill 555-4445.

Terrarium. Fish-tank style. Already planted and doing great! Several sizes and kinds. Not much maintenance needed. I make them and sell them. I can tell you how to keep the plants healthy. From $10 to $50. Terence 555-2390.

**TO TRADE**

CD-Rom's. I've got 8 CD-Rom Games. Willing to trade them for ones I haven't tried. Mac compatible. Beth 555-9666.

Stamps from all over the world. Special Editions. A one-year collection. Show me yours. Let's trade! Call Peter 555-4690.

Marionette. This guy is cute! Hiking shorts, a little cap. You control the strings. It was a present, brought from Austria. Would like to trade him for an American doll with wardrobe. Barbara 555-5111.

Marble Collection. Cat's-Eyes, Clears, Blacks, and More! Also like to play marbles. Call me Saturday and bring your collection. We'll swap and play. Barnaby 555-8690

**WANTED**

Bike Parts Needed. I repair bikes and then give them to people who need them. Call if you have tires, handlebars, wheels, or gears to sell. Nothing is in too bad a condition! Can also pay small amounts for complete bikes in need of repair. Call Justin. 555-9870

Food and Volunteers. We're a one-kitchen operation making meals for the needy. We could use cold-cuts, fruit, beverages, or any other food donations. We also need some help putting it all together! 555-1111.

**SERVICES**

Tutors. Having trouble with one of your subjects? Don't despair. We're a team of student volunteers who tutor after school in Mr. Barkley's room. Call Patti at 555-9128.

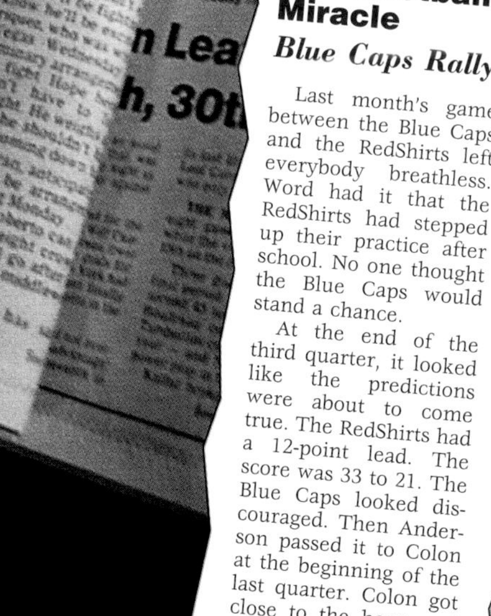

## Sports

### A Basketball Miracle

*Blue Caps Rally*

Last month's game between the Blue Caps and the RedShirts left everybody breathless. Word had it that the RedShirts had stepped up their practice after school. No one thought the Blue Caps would stand a chance.

At the end of the third quarter, it looked like the predictions were about to come true. The RedShirts had a 12-point lead. The score was 33 to 21. The Blue Caps looked discouraged. Then Anderson passed it to Colon at the beginning of the last quarter. Colon got close to the hoop and put it home. After that the Blue Caps rallied, creaming the Redshirts by a margin of 9. The final score was Blue Caps 44, RedShirts 35.

This glossary can help you to pronounce and find out the meanings of words in this book that you may not know.

The words are listed in alphabetical order. Guide words at the top of each page tell you the first and last words on the page.

Each word is divided into syllables. The way to pronounce each word is given next. You can understand the pronunciation respelling by using the key at right. A shorter key appears at the bottom of every other page.

When a word has more than one syllable, a dark accent mark (**′**) shows which syllable is stressed. In some words, a light accent mark (′) shows which syllable has a less heavy stress.

Glossary entries are based on entries in *The Macmillan/McGraw-Hill School Dictionary 1.*

**a** at, bad
**ā** ape, pain, day, break
**ä** father, car, heart
**âr** care, pair, bear, their, where
**e** end, pet, said, heaven, friend
**ē** equal, me, feet, team, piece, key
**i** it, big, English, hymn
**ī** ice, fine, lie, my
**îr** ear, deer, here, pierce
**o** odd, hot, watch
**ō** old, oat, toe, low
**ô** coffee, all, taught, law, fought
**ôr** order, fork, horse, story, pour
**oi** oil, toy
**ou** out, now
**u** up, mud, love, double
**ū** use, mule, cue, feud, few
**ü** rule, true, food
**u̇** put, wood, should
**ûr** burn, hurry, term, bird, word, courage
**ə** about, taken, pencil, lemon, circus
**b** bat, above, job
**ch** chin, such, match
**d** dear, soda, bad
**f** five, defend, leaf, off, cough, elephant
**g** game, ago, fog, egg
**h** hat, ahead
**hw** white, whether, which
**j** joke, enjoy, gem, page, edge
**k** kite, bakery, seek, tack, cat
**l** lid, sailor, feel, ball, allow
**m** man, family, dream
**n** not, final, pan, knife
**ng** long, singer, pink
**p** pail, repair, soap, happy
**r** ride, parent, wear, more, marry
**s** sit, aside, pets, cent, pass
**sh** shoe, washer, fish, mission, nation
**t** tag, pretend, fat, button, dressed
**th** thin, panther, both
**t͟h** this, mother, smooth
**v** very, favor, wave
**w** wet, weather, reward
**y** yes, onion
**z** zoo, lazy, jazz, rose, dogs, houses
**zh** vision, treasure, seizure

**abandoned** Left behind; no longer used or lived in. The porch of the *abandoned* house is overgrown with vines.
**a•ban•doned** (ə ban′dənd) *adjective.*

**accurate** Being correct, exact, or precise. The newspaper stories about the accident were not *accurate.*
**ac•cu•rate** (ak′yər it) *adjective.*

**achievement** Something accomplished or carried out. The invention of the telephone was a great *achievement.*
**a•chieve•ment** (ə chēv′mənt) *noun, plural* **achievements.**

**admission 1.** The price a person must pay to enter. The *admission* to the park was one dollar. **2.** The act of allowing to enter. Who is in charge of the *admission* of patients to that hospital?
**ad•mis•sion** (ad mish′ən) *noun, plural* **admissions.**

*admission*

**advantage** Something that is helpful or useful; benefit. Being tall is an *advantage* for a basketball player.
• **to take advantage of. 1.** To use in a helpful or beneficial way; benefit by. We *took advantage of* the excellent opportunity to learn French. **2.** To use or treat in an unfair or selfish way. Don't *take advantage of* your friend's willingness to be helpful.
**ad•van•tage** (ad van′tij) *noun, plural* **advantages.**

**afford 1.** To have enough money to pay for. Can you *afford* a new car? **2.** To be able to spare or give. They couldn't *afford* the time to help us. **3.** To be able to do without causing harm. I can't *afford* to skip breakfast.
**af•ford** (ə fôrd′) *verb,* **afforded, affording.**

**Albertosaurus** (al bûr′tə sôr′əs).

**alien 1.** A being from some place outside of the earth or its atmosphere. The movie was about *aliens* who tried to take over the earth. **2.** A person who is not a citizen of the country in which he or she lives; foreigner.
**al•ien** (āl′yən *or* a′lē ən) *noun, plural* **aliens.**

**Allosaurus** (al′ə sôr′əs).

**anchor** A heavy metal device that is attached to a ship by a chain or cable. When an *anchor* is dropped overboard, it digs into the ground below the water and keeps the ship from drifting.
• **at anchor** held fast by an anchor.
**an•chor** (ang′kər) *noun, plural* **anchors.**

**Apatosaurus** (ə pat′ə sôr′əs).

**apiece** For or to each one; each. These red pencils are fifteen cents *apiece.*
**a•piece** (ə pēs′) *adverb.*

**Appalachians** A mountain range reaching from Canada to Alabama.
**Ap•pa•la•chi•ans** (ap′ə lā′chē ənz) *noun, plural.*

**approve** **1.** To have or give a favorable opinion. My parents don't *approve* of my staying up very late. **2.** To consent or agree to officially; authorize. The town recently *approved* the construction of a public swimming pool.
**ap•prove** (ə prüv′) *verb,* **approved, approving.**

**aquatic** Growing or living in or near water. Most frogs are *aquatic* animals.
**a•quat•ic** (ə kwat′ik *or* ə kwot′ik) *adjective.*

**arctic** Having to do with the ice-covered region surrounding the North Pole.
**arc•tic** (ärk′tik) *adjective.*

*arctic*

**arrest** **1.** To seize and hold by authority of the law. The police officer *arrested* the suspect. **2.** To stop or hold. We hope to *arrest* pollution in our country.
**ar•rest** (ə rest′) *verb,* **arrested, arresting.**

**artificial** Made by people, not by nature; not natural.
**ar•ti•fi•cial** (är′tə fish′əl) *adjective.*

**assemble** To come or bring together. A crowd began to *assemble.*
**as•sem•ble** (ə sem′bəl) *verb,* **assembled, assembling.**

**asteroid** Any of the thousands of small planets that revolve around the sun. Most are between the orbits of Mars and Jupiter.
**as•ter•oid** (as′tə roid′) *noun, plural* **asteroids.**

**astonish** To surprise very much; amaze. The news that I had won the contest *astonished* me.
**as•ton•ish** (ə ston′ish) *verb,* **astonished, astonishing.**

**Ate** The word for "father" in the language of the Lakota people.
**A•te** (ä ta′) *noun.*

**athletic** Of or having to do with games, sports, or activities that take strength, skill, and speed.
**ath•let•ic** (ath let′ik) *adjective.*

**atmosphere** **1.** The layer of gases that surrounds the Earth. The *atmosphere* is made up of oxygen, nitrogen, carbon dioxide, and other gases. **2.** Character or mood. Our house has a happy *atmosphere.*
**at•mos•phere** (at′məs fîr′) *noun, plural* **atmospheres.**

**attempt** To make an effort; try. The kitten *attempted* to follow the squirrel up the tree.
**at•tempt** (ə tempt′) *verb,* **attempted, attempting.**

at; āpe; fär; câre; end; mē; it; īce; pîerce; hot; ōld; sông; fôrk; oil; out; up; ūse; rüle; pu̇ll; tûrn; chin; sing; shop; thin; th̲is; hw in white; zh in treasure. The symbol ə stands for the unstressed vowel sound in about, taken, pencil, lemon, and circus.

**attract** To draw by gaining the attention or admiration of. The beautiful scenery in these mountains *attracts* many tourists.
**at•tract** (ə trakt′) *verb,* **attracted, attracting.**

**attractive** Having a quality that attracts people; appealing; pleasing. He looked very *attractive* in his new suit.
**at•trac•tive** (ə trak′tiv) *adjective.*

**auction** To sell at a public sale at which articles or property are sold to the person who offers the most money. *Verb.*
—A public sale at which things are auctioned. *Noun.*
**auc•tion** (ôk′shən) *noun, plural* **auctions;** *verb,* **auctioned, auctioning.**

*auction*

**authority 1.** A good source of information or facts. That professor is an *authority* on the life of Abraham Lincoln. **2.** The power or right to make decisions, command, act, or control. The captain has *authority* over all the sailors on a ship.
**au•thor•i•ty** (ə thôr′i tē) *noun, plural* **authorities.**

**automatically 1.** By itself. The dishwasher operates *automatically.* **2.** Without a person's control. Digestion is an action of the body that occurs *automatically.*
**au•to•mat•i•cal•ly** (ô′tə mat′ik lē) *adverb.*

**avalanche** The swift, sudden fall of a mass of snow, ice, earth, or rocks down a mountain slope. The *avalanche* completely covered the village with mud.
**av•a•lanche** (av′ə lanch′) *noun, plural* **avalanches.**

# B

**bachelor** A man who has never been married.
**bach•e•lor** (bach′ə lər) *noun, plural* **bachelors.**

**backwoods** Heavily wooded areas far from centers of population. We didn't expect to find a cabin hidden away in the *backwoods.*
**back•woods** (bak′wudz) *noun, plural.*

**Barosaurus** (bar′ə sôr′əs).

**Baryonyx** (bar′ē on′iks).

**bashful** Embarrassed and shy around people. The *bashful* child hid behind the chair when the babysitter arrived.
**bash•ful** (bash′fəl) *adjective.*

**basis** The part that something rests on or depends on; foundation. The idea that toads give you warts has no *basis* in fact.
**ba•sis** (bā′sis) *noun, plural* **bases** (bā′sez).

**beloved** Loved very much. The friendly dog was *beloved* by the whole neighborhood.
**be•lov•ed** (bi luv'id *or* bi luvd') *adjective.*

**big top** The main tent of a circus.
**big top** (big top) *noun, plural* **big tops.**

**blurt** To say suddenly or without thinking. I was sorry after I *blurted* out the secret.
**blurt** (blûrt) *verb,* **blurted, blurting.**

**board** To get a room to sleep in and meals for pay. I *boarded* with a family in France last summer.
**board** (bôrd) *verb,* **boarded, boarding.**

**border 1.** To lie on the edge of. California *borders* Oregon. **2.** To put an edging on. The handkerchief was *bordered* with lace.
**bor•der** (bôr'dər) *verb,* **bordered, bordering.**

**Brachiosaurus** (bra'ke ō sôr' s *or* brak'ə ō sôr'əs).

**Brontosaurus** A huge plant-eating dinosaur.
**bron•to•sau•rus** (bron'tə sôr'əs) *noun, plural* **brontosauri** *or* **brontosauruses.**

*brontosaurus*

**bruise** To cause an injury that does not break the skin but makes a bluish or blackish mark on it. *Verb.*
—A mark made by such an injury. *Noun.*
**bruise** (brüz) *noun, plural* **bruises;** *verb,* **bruised, bruising.**

**burglar** A person who breaks into a house, store, or other place to steal something. *Burglars* broke into the hotel room and stole some valuable jewels.
**bur•glar** (bûr'glər) *noun, plural* **burglars.**

# C

**calypso** An improvised song, originally from the British West Indies, usually dealing with subjects that are humorous or of current interest.
**ca•lyp•so** (kə lip'sō) *noun, plural* **calypsos.**

**Word History**

The music known as **calypso** takes its name from Calypso, a sea nymph in Greek mythology. Calypso fell in love with the hero Ulysses when, in his wanderings, he visited her island. He remained with her for seven years.

at; āpe; fär; câre; end; mē; it; īce; pîerce; hot; ōld; sông; fôrk; oil; out; up; ūse; rüle; pu̇ll; tûrn; chin; sing; shop; thin; th̲is; hw in white; zh in treasure. The symbol ə stands for the unstressed vowel sound in about, taken, pencil, lemon, and circus.

**Camarasaurus** (kam′ə rə sôr′əs).

**Canowicakte** (chä no′wa chäk ta).

**canvas** A strong, heavy cloth made of cotton, flax, or hemp. It is used to make things that must be strong and last for a long time. Tents, sails, coats, and boat covers are made of *canvas.*
**can•vas** (kan′vəs) *noun, plural* **canvases.**

**captive** Held prisoner. The *captive* lion was kept in a cage.
**cap•tive** (kap′tiv) *adjective.*

**capture** **1.** To succeed in showing or expressing something. The story *captures* what it is like to be an only child. **2.** To attract and hold. The film's strange title *captured* my interest.
**cap•ture** (kap′chər) *verb,* **captured, capturing.**

**carnival** A fair or festival that has games, rides, and other amusements. A special roller coaster was built just for the city's spring *carnival.*
**car•ni•val** (kär′nə vəl) *noun, plural* **carnivals.**

*carnival*

**cemetery** A place where the dead are buried.
**cem•e•ter•y** (sem′ə ter′ē) *noun, plural* **cemeteries.**

**Ceratosaurus** (se rat′ə sôr′əs).

**certificate** A written statement that is accepted as proof of certain facts. Your birth *certificate* tells when and where you were born.
**cer•tif•i•cate** (sər tif′i kit) *noun, plural* **certificates.**

**Chan** A Japanese form of address for a child, used following the name.
**Chan** (chän) *noun.*

**Chano** (chä′nō).

**civilization** A condition of human society in which government, art, and science are highly developed. Civilization is often characterized by the use of writing and the growth of cities. In school we study the *civilization* of ancient Egypt.
**civ•i•li•za•tion** (siv′ə lə zā′shən) *noun, plural* **civilizations.**

**clammy** Cold and damp. They walked through the *clammy* basement.
**clam•my** (klam′ē) *adjective.*

**collision** The act of crashing against each other. The two bicycle riders had a *collision,* but neither one was hurt.
**col•li•sion** (kə lizh′ən) *noun, plural* **collisions.**

**conceal** To put or keep out of sight; hide. Don't forget to *conceal* the house keys under the porch. I *concealed* my disappointment by smiling.
**con•ceal** (kən sēl′) *verb,* **concealed, concealing.**

**concentrate** To bring together into one place. The population of our country is *concentrated* in the cities.
**con•cen•trate** (kon′sən trāt′) *verb,* **concentrated, concentrating.**

**congratulate** To give good wishes or praise for someone's success or for something nice that has happened. We *congratulated* them on doing such a good job on their science project.
**con•grat•u•late** (kən grach'ə lāt') *verb,* **congratulated, congratulating.**

**consent** To give permission or agree to. My parents would not *consent* to my going camping by myself, so they went camping with me.
**con•sent** (kən sent') *verb,* **consented, consenting.**

**constitution** The basic principles used to govern a state, country, or organization. The people voted for numerous changes in their state's *constitution.*
**con•sti•tu•tion** (kon'sti tü'shən) *noun, plural* **constitutions.**

**contrary 1.** Liking to argue and oppose. That *contrary* child never agrees with what other people say. **2.** Entirely different; opposite. My younger cousin's ideas about sports and music are *contrary* to my own. • **on the contrary.** Just the opposite of what has been said. You are not a clumsy dancer; *on the contrary,* you are very graceful.
**con•trar•y** (kən trâr'ē *or* kon'trer ē *for definition 1;* kon'trer ē *for definition 2) adjective.*

**contrast** To show differences that are based on comparing. The teacher *contrasted* life in a big city and life on a farm. *Verb.*
—A difference. There is a great *contrast* between the weather at the North Pole and the weather in the tropics. *Noun.*
**con•trast** (kən trast' *for verb;* kon'trast *for noun) noun, plural* **contrasts;** *verb,* **contrasted, contrasting.**

**convenience** Ease and comfort. I like the *convenience* of canned foods.
**con•ven•ience** (kən vēn'yəns) *noun, plural* **conveniences.**

**cramp**[1] To cause a sharp pain in a muscle. Holding the pencil tightly for so long *cramped* my hand. *Verb.*
—A sharp pain in a muscle that suddenly gets tight. A *cramp* in the leg forced the runner to leave the race. *Noun.*
**cramp** (kramp) *noun, plural* **cramps;** *verb,* **cramped, cramping.**

**cramp**[2] To limit; confine. The tiny amount of space on the boat *cramped* us.
**cramp** (kramp) *verb,* **cramped, cramping.**

**crank** A part of a machine that has a handle attached to a rod. When the handle is turned, the rod turns with it and makes the machine work. The storekeeper turned the *crank* of the store's awning to lower it. *Noun.*
—To turn a *crank* so that something will work. *Verb.*
**crank** (krangk) *noun, plural* **cranks;** *verb,* **cranked, cranking.**

**credit 1.** Praise or honor. The person who did most of the cooking deserves *credit* for the dinner. **2.** Belief in the truth of something; faith. Nobody gave full *credit* to the strange story. **3.** Trust in a person to pay a debt later. Several stores have given me *credit*
**cred•it** (kred'it) *noun, plural* **credits.**

at; āpe; fär; câre; end; mē; it; īce; pîerce; hot; ōld; sông; fôrk; oil; out; up; ūse; rüle; pu̇ll; tûrn; chin; sing; shop; thin; th̲is; hw in white; zh in treasure. The symbol ə stands for the unstressed vowel sound in about, taken, pencil, lemon, and circus.

**crinkle** To form or cause to form wrinkles or ripples; wrinkle; crumple. The paper *crinkled* in the fire and then burst into flame.
**crin•kle** (kring'kəl) *verb,* **crinkled, crinkling.**

**critical** Finding something wrong with things. You were *critical* of every plan that we suggested.
**crit•i•cal** (krit'i kəl) *adjective.*

**crutch** A support that assists a person in walking. A crutch is a pole that usually has a padded part at the top that fits under the arm so a person can lean on it.
**crutch** (kruch) *noun, plural* **crutches.**

*crutch*

**current** A part of the air or of a body of water that is moving along in a path. The rubber raft was caught in the *current* and carried out to sea.
**cur•rent** (kûr'ənt) *noun, plural* **currents.**

**cycle 1.** A series of events that happen one after another in the same order, over and over again. Spring, summer, autumn, and winter are the *cycle* of the four seasons of the year. **2.** A bicycle, tricycle, or motorcycle.
**cy•cle** (si'kəl) *noun, plural* **cycles.**

# D

**dangle** To hang or swing loosely. Some old kite string *dangled* from a branch of the tree.
**dan•gle** (dang'gəl) *verb,* **dangled, dangling.**

**data** Individual facts, figures, and other items of information. These *data* from the computer don't seem to be accurate.
**da•ta** (dā'tə *or* dat'ə) *noun, plural.*

**dawdle** To waste time; linger.
**daw•dle** (dô'dəl) *verb,* **dawdled, dawdling.**

**decade** A period of ten years.
**dec•ade** (dek'ād) *noun, plural* **decades.**

**decipher** To figure out the meaning of something that is difficult to read or understand. No one could *decipher* the scribbled handwriting.
**de•ci•pher** (di sī'fər) *verb,* **deciphered, deciphering.**

**defend 1.** To guard against attack or danger; protect. A goalie's job is to *defend* the goal against the opposing team. **2.** To speak or act in support of. The lawyer agreed to *defend* the man.
**de•fend** (di fend') *verb,* **defended, defending.**

**Deinonychus** (di non'ə kəs).

**delivery 1.** The act of carrying or taking something to the proper place or person. The mail carrier makes a mail *delivery* every day except Sundays and holidays. **2.** A way of speaking or singing. The singer's *delivery* was loud.
**de•liv•er•y** (di liv'ə rē) *noun, plural* **deliveries.**

**Delphine** (del fēn′).

**demolish** To tear down or destroy. The workers *demolished* the old factory to make way for a new office building.
**de•mol•ish** (di mol′ish) *verb,* **demolished, demolishing.**

*demolish*

**deposit** To put or set down; place. The shopper *deposited* the groceries on the kitchen table.
**de•pos•it** (di poz′it) *verb,* **deposited, depositing.**

**despair** A complete loss of hope. The family was filled with *despair* when the fire destroyed their house.
**de•spair** (di spâr′) *noun.*

**destruction** Great damage or ruin. The earthquake caused widespread *destruction.*
**de•struc•tion** (di struk′shən) *noun.*

**developer** A person who builds houses or other buildings on an area of land.
**de•vel•op•er** (di vəl′ə pər) *noun, plural* **developers.**

**development 1.** A group of houses or other buildings on a large area of land. The houses often look alike and are built by one builder. **2.** The act or process of bringing or coming gradually into being. The *development* of a spacecraft that could reach the moon took many years.
**de•vel•op•ment** (di vel′əp mənt) *noun, plural* **developments.**

**digest** To break down food in the mouth, stomach, and intestines. When we *digest* food, we change it into a form that can be absorbed and used by the body.
**di•gest** (di jest′ *or* dī jest′) *verb,* **digested, digesting.**

**Diplodocus** (di plod′ə kəs).

**disaster** An event that causes much suffering or loss. The flood was a *disaster.*
**dis•as•ter** (di zas′tər) *noun, plural* **disasters.**

**discount** An amount subtracted from the regular price. I bought a suit on sale at a 25 percent *discount.*
**dis•count** (dis′kount) *noun, plural* **discounts.**

**distinguish** To know or show that there is a difference between certain things.
**dis•tin•guish** (di sting′gwish) *verb,* **distinguished, distinguishing.**

**distressed** Having or showing pain, sorrow, or misery. The *distressed* woman asked the police for help.
**dis•tressed** (di strest′) *adjective.*

> **a**t; **â**pe; f**ä**r; c**à**re; **e**nd; m**ê**; **i**t; **î**ce; p**ì**erce; h**o**t; **ô**ld; s**ò**ng; f**ò**rk; **oi**l; **ou**t; **u**p; **û**se; r**ü**le; p°ll; t**ù**rn; **ch**in; si**ng**; **sh**op; **th**in; **th**is; **hw** in **wh**ite; **zh** in trea**s**ure. The symbol ə stands for the unstressed vowel sound in **a**bout, tak**e**n, penc**i**l, lem**o**n, and circ**u**s.

**district** An area that is a special part of a larger area. That store is in the business *district* of the city.
**dis•trict** (dis'trikt) *noun, plural* **districts.**

**District, the** The District of Columbia, the location of the capital of the United States.
**Dis•trict** (dis'trikt) *noun.*

**division 1.** One of the parts into which something is split up; a group or section. Our baseball team belongs to the Eastern *Division.* **2.** The process of dividing two numbers to show how many times one number contains the other. We were learning multiplication and *division* in our math class.
**di•vi•sion** (di vizh'ən) *noun, plural* **divisions.**

**document** A written or printed statement that gives official proof and information about something.
**doc•u•ment** (dok'yə mənt) *noun, plural* **documents.**

**Doña Josefa** (don'yä ho sā'fä).

**donate** To give; contribute. The family *donated* their old clothes to people who needed them.
**do•nate** (dō'nāt) *verb,* **donated, donating.**

**Doshita?** Japanese for "What is wrong?"
**Do•shi•ta** (dosh'tə').

**drawbridge** A kind of bridge that can be raised or moved so that ships can pass under it. They raised the *drawbridge* so that the tall sailboat could pass.
**draw•bridge** (drô'brij') *noun, plural* **drawbridges.**

**drizzle** To rain steadily in fine, misty drops. We had expected a downpour, but it only *drizzled. Verb.* —A fine, misty rain. *Noun.*
**driz•zle** (driz'əl) *verb,* **drizzled, drizzling;** *noun, plural* **drizzles.**

**drought** A long period of time when there is very little rain, or no rain at all.
**drought** (drout) *noun, plural* **droughts.**

**Earp, Wyatt** A lawman and gunfighter in the American West in the 1800s.
**Wy•att Earp** (wī'ət ûrp)

**elegant** Rich and fine in quality. The museum has a display of *elegant* costumes.
**el•e•gant** (el'i gənt) *adjective.*

*emerge*

**emerge 1.** To come into view. The sun *emerged* from behind a cloud. **2.** To come out; become known. New facts about the case *emerged* during the trial.
**e•merge** (i mûrj') *verb,* **emerged, emerging.**

**enchantment** The state of being delighted, charmed, or fascinated.
**en•chant•ment** (en chant′mənt) *noun, plural* **enchantments.**

**entertain 1.** To keep interested and amused. The clown *entertained* the children. **2.** To have as a guest. They often *entertain* people in their house in the country.
**en•ter•tain** (en′tər tān′) *verb,* **entertained, entertaining.**

**erect** To build. A new apartment house will be *erected* on that lot. *Verb.*
—Upright; raised. The dog's ears became *erect* when its owner whistled. *Adjective.*
**e•rect** (i rekt′) *verb,* **erected, erecting;** *adjective.*

**eureka** A word used as an exclamation upon the sudden discovery of something or the solving of a problem.
**eu•re•ka** (yu̇ rē′kə) *interjection.*

**Word History**

**Eureka** comes from the Greek word *heureka*, which means "I have found (it)." The Greek scientist Archimedes supposedly said this when he discovered a method for determining the purity of gold.

**exhaustion** The condition of being very weak or tired. The runner's *exhaustion* was caused by a twenty-mile run.
**ex•haus•tion** (eg zôs′chən) *noun.*

**expense 1.** Money spent to buy or do something; cost. My family cannot afford the *expense* of a new car. **2.** A cause or reason for spending money. Building the swimming pool was a big *expense.*
**ex•pense** (ek spens′) *noun, plural* **expenses.**

**expression 1.** The act of putting thoughts or feelings into words or actions. These flowers are an *expression* of our thanks to you. **2.** An outward show; look. The students all had *expressions* of surprise on their faces after the magician performed the trick.
**ex•pres•sion** (ek spresh′ən) *noun, plural* **expressions.**

**flail** To wave or swing, especially violently or quickly. I *flailed* my arms at the bees swarming around me.
**flail** (flāl) *verb,* **flailed, flailing.**

**flexible 1.** Able to bend without breaking; not stiff. **2.** Able to change or adjust when necessary.
**flex•i•ble** (flek′sə bəl) *adjective.*

**fossil** The hardened remains or traces of an animal or plant that lived long ago. The *fossils* that we found were imprints of ancient leaves and seashells in rock.
**fos•sil** (fos′əl) *noun, plural* **fossils.**

**fragile** Easily broken; delicate. That china cup is very *fragile.*
**frag•ile** (fraj′əl) *adjective.*

at; āpe; fär; câre; end; mē; it; īce; pîerce; hot; ōld; sông; fôrk; oil; out; up; ūse; rüle; pu̇ll; tûrn; chin; sing; shop; thin; th̲is; hw in white; zh in treasure. The symbol ə stands for the unstressed vowel sound in about, taken, pencil, lemon, and circus.

# G

**gigantic** Like a giant; huge and powerful. A *gigantic* whale swam under the ship.
**gi•gan•tic** (jī gan'tik) *adjective.*

*gigantic*

**glory** Great praise; honor; fame. They both did the work, but only one got the *glory.*
**glo•ry** (glôr'ē) *noun, plural* **glories.**

**graffiti** Words or drawings on walls, fences, sidewalks, and so forth.
**graf•fi•ti** (grə fē'tē) *noun, plural.*

**Word History**

The word **graffiti** has a long history. It comes from the Italian word *graffiare,* which means "to scratch." The Italian word goes back to the Latin word *graphium,* meaning "stylus," or an instrument used for writing on soft materials, such as wax. The Latin word, in turn, comes from the Greek word *graphein,* which means "to write."

**gratitude** A feeling of thanks for a favor one has received or for something that makes one happy. Our neighbors were full of *gratitude* for the help that we gave them.
**grat•i•tude** (grat'i tüd' *or* grat'i tūd') *noun.*

**gravity 1.** The force that pulls things toward the center of the earth. Gravity is the force that causes objects to fall when they are dropped. Gravity causes objects to have weight. **2.** Serious nature. Because of the *gravity* of the situation, troops were sent in.
**grav•i•ty** (grav'i tē) *noun, plural* **gravities.**

**Great Depression** The period of hard times in the United States that began in 1929 and lasted throughout the 1930s. During the *Great Depression,* many people lost their jobs and many businesses closed.
**Great De•pres•sion** (grāt di presh'ən) *noun.*

**Great Plains** A large region east of the Rocky Mountains, reaching from Canada to Texas, and consisting primarily of flat or rolling, mostly treeless plains.
**Great Plains** (grāt plānz) *noun.*

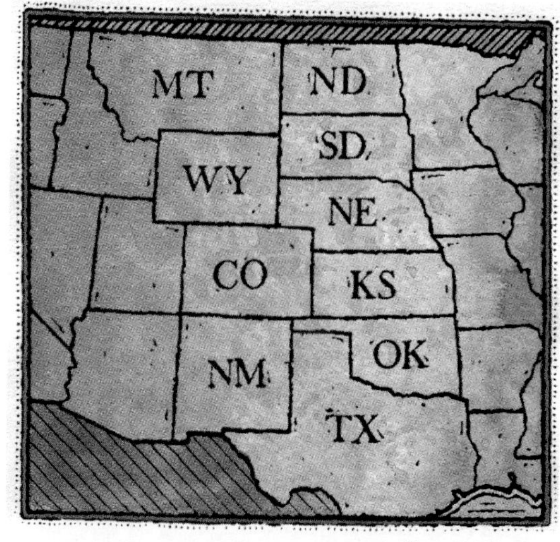

*Great Plains*

**grope** **1.** To feel about with the hands. The child *groped* for the light switch in the dark room. **2.** To search for something in a blind or uncertain way. The students *groped* for the right answer while the teacher waited for someone to raise a hand.
**grope** (grōp) *verb,* **groped, groping.**

**guarantee** **1.** To give a promise to repair or replace something or to give back the money for it, if anything goes wrong with it before a certain time has passed. The company *guarantees* this dishwasher for one year. **2.** To make sure or certain. Having that band play will *guarantee* that the dance will be a success.
**guar•an•tee** (gar′ən tē′) *verb,* **guaranteed, guaranteeing.**

**Gulf of Mexico** The large body of water mostly surrounded by the United States and Mexico.
**Gulf of Mex•i•co** (gulf əv mek′si kō′) *noun.*

**heritage** Something that is handed down from earlier generations or from the past; tradition. The right to free speech is part of the American *heritage.*
**her•it•age** (her′i tij) *noun, plural* **heritages.**

**historian** A person who knows a great deal about the story or record of what has happened in the past.
**his•to•ri•an** (hi stôr′ē ən) *noun, plural* **historians.**

**hoist** To lift or pull up. We *hoisted* the flag up the pole.
**hoist** (hoist) *verb,* **hoisted, hoisting.**

**honorable** Bringing honor or distinction; creditable.
**hon•or•a•ble** (on′ər ə bəl) *adjective.*

**House of Representatives** One of the two lawmaking groups that make up the United States Congress.
**House of Rep•re•sent•a•tives** (hous əv rep′ri zen′tə tivz) *noun.*

*House of Representatives*

**hover** To stay close by. The reporters *hovered* around the candidate while waiting to ask their questions.
**hov•er** (huv′ər *or* hov′ər) *verb,* **hovered, hovering.**

at; āpe; fär; câre; end; mē; it; īce; pîerce; hot; ōld; sông; fôrk; oil; out; up; ūse; rüle; pu̇ll; tûrn; chin; sing; shop; thin; this; hw in white; zh in treasure. The symbol ə stands for the unstressed vowel sound in about, taken, pencil, lemon, and circus.

# I

**incorrect** Not right or correct; not proper. You must do this problem over because your answer is *incorrect.*
**in•cor•rect** (in′kə rekt′) *adjective.*
**incorrectly** *adverb.*

**injure** To cause harm to; damage or hurt. I *injured* myself when I fell.
**in•jure** (in′jər) *verb,* **injured, injuring.**

**insistent** Demanding attention or notice. The *insistent* ringing of the doorbell woke us.
**in•sis•tent** (in sis′tənt) *adjective.*

**intense** **1.** Very great or strong, extreme. The heat from the iron was so *intense* that it burned a hole in the cloth. **2.** Having or showing strong feeling, purpose, or effort; concentrated. The worried parent had an *intense* look.
**in•tense** (in tens′) *adjective.*

**intention** A purpose; plan. Our *intention* is to wash all the windows before dinner.
**in•ten•tion** (in ten′shən) *noun, plural* **intentions.**

**interpret** **1.** To explain the meaning of. The teacher *interpreted* what the author meant in the poem. **2.** To change from one language to another; translate. Since my friends couldn't speak Spanish, I *interpreted* what my Mexican cousin was saying.
**in•ter•pret** (in tûr′prit) *verb,* **interpreted, interpreting.**

**invade** To go into or to attack in order to conquer. Enemy troops *invaded* the country.
**in•vade** (in vād′) *verb,* **invaded, invading.**

# J

**James, Frank and Jesse** Two outlaw brothers who robbed banks and trains in and around Missouri in the 1800s.
**James, Frank and Jesse** (frangk, jese jamz)

**Jericho** An ancient Palestinian city in Jordan near the northern tip of the Dead Sea.
**Jer•i•cho** (jer′i kō′) *noun.*

**Jerusalem** A historic city in Palestine, the capital of Israel.
**Je•ru•sa•lem** (jə rü′sə ləm) *noun.*

**jut** To stick out. The lighthouse is on a piece of land that *juts* into the sea.
**jut** (jut) *verb,* **jutted, jutting.**

**kernel** **1.** The whole grain or seed of wheat, corn, and some other plants. When we eat corn on the cob, we are eating the *kernels.* **2.** The central or most necessary part. There was a *kernel* of truth in what our opponent had said.
▲ Another word that sounds like this is **colonel.**
**ker•nel** (kûr′nəl) *noun, plural* **kernels.**

**Klondike** A region in the Yukon Territory of northwestern Canada.
**Klon•dike** (klon′dīk′) *noun.*

# L

**Lakota-oyate** (lä kō'tä ō yä'ta').

**landscape** The stretch of land that can be seen from a place; view.
**land•scape** (land'skāp') *noun, plural* **landscapes.**

**lecture 1.** To scold. The teacher *lectured* us for not doing our homework. **2.** To give a talk to an audience. The mayor *lectured* on the history of our town.
**lec•ture** (lek'chər) *verb,* **lectured, lecturing.**

**legendary** Of or having to do with a story that is passed down through the years that many people believe, but that is not entirely true.
**leg•end•ar•y** (lej'ən der'ē) *adjective.*

**Leigh** (lē).

**limerick** A funny poem five lines long. The following is an example of a *limerick:* There once was a man named Paul/Who went to a masquerade ball./He decided to risk it/And go as a biscuit/But a dog ate him up in the hall.
**lim•er•ick** (lim'ər ik) *noun, plural* **limericks.**

**Word History**

The kind of poem called a **limerick,** which has existed since Roman times, takes its name from Limerick, a county and village in Ireland. In the late 1890s, making up these amusing poems became a popular form of entertainment at parties.

**Lupe** (lü'pā).

# M

**Mamenchisaurus** (mə men'chi sôr'əs).

**management** The act or process of directing or controlling. The business failed because of bad *management.*
**man•age•ment** (man'ij mənt) *noun.*

**marking** A mark or marks; patch or patches of color. The bird had brown and white *markings* on its wings.
**mark•ing** (mär'king) *noun, plural* **markings.**

**microscope** A device that is used to look at things that are too small to be seen with the naked eye. It has one or more lenses that produce an enlarged image of anything seen through it. The biologist studied the leaf under a *microscope.*
**mi•cro•scope** (mī'krə skōp') *noun, plural* **microscopes.**

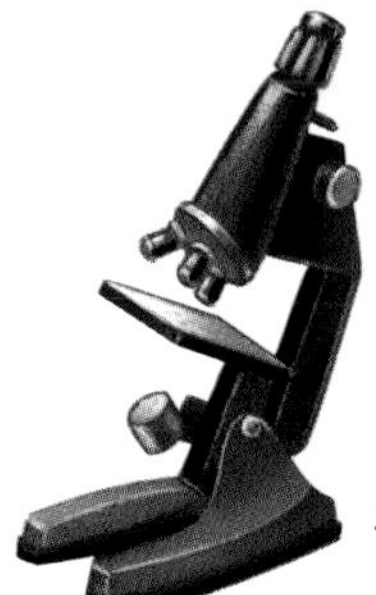

*microscope*

at; āpe; fär; câre; end; mē; it; īce; pîerce; hot; ōld; sông; fôrk; oil; out; up; ūse; rüle; pu̇ll; tûrn; chin; sing; shop; thin; th̲is; hw in white; zh in treasure. The symbol ə stands for the unstressed vowel sound in about, taken, pencil, lemon, and circus.

**millionaire** A person who has money or property worth a million or more dollars.
**mil•lion•aire** (mil′yə nâr′) *noun, plural* **millionaires.**

**miniature** Much smaller than the usual size. My parents made *miniature* furniture for my doll house. *Adjective.*
—A model or copy of something in a much smaller size. We bought a Statue of Liberty *miniature* as a souvenir of our trip to New York. *Noun.*
**min•i•a•ture** (min′ē ə chər) *adjective; noun, plural* **miniatures.**

**miserably** In a very unhappy or wretched way. I failed *miserably* at my first attempt to ice-skate.
**mis•er•a•bly** (miz′ər ə blē) *adverb.*

**monitor** To watch over or observe something. Our teacher *monitored* the fire drill. *Verb.*
—**1.** A student who is given a special duty to do. **2.** The screen that a computer uses to display numbers, letters, and pictures. *Noun.*
**mon•i•tor** (mon′i tər) *noun, plural* **monitors;** *verb,* **monitored, monitoring.**

**monstrous** Horrible or frightening. The dragon in the story was a *monstrous* creature.
**mon•strous** (mon′strəs) *adjective.*

**mozzarella** A soft, white cheese of Italian origin with a mild flavor.
**moz•za•rel•la** (mot′sə rel′ə *or* mōt′sə rel′ə) *noun.*

**Word History**

The word **mozzarella** comes from Italy. In Italian, *mozzarella* means "little slices." In cooking, *mozzarella* cheese is often cut up into small pieces so that it will melt quickly.

**murky** Dark and gloomy. We couldn't see beneath the surface of the *murky* water in the pond.
**murk•y** (mûr′kē) *adjective,* **murkier, murkiest.**

**mustache** Hair that grows above the upper lip. My grandfather has a big *mustache* that curls up at each end. This word is also spelled **moustache.**
**mus•tache** (mus′tash *or* mə stash′) *noun, plural* **mustaches.**

# N

**Nanotyrannus** (nan′ō ti ran′əs).

**newborn** A baby born very recently. A *newborn* baby sleeps most of the time.
**new•born** (nü′bôrn) *noun, plural* **newborns.**

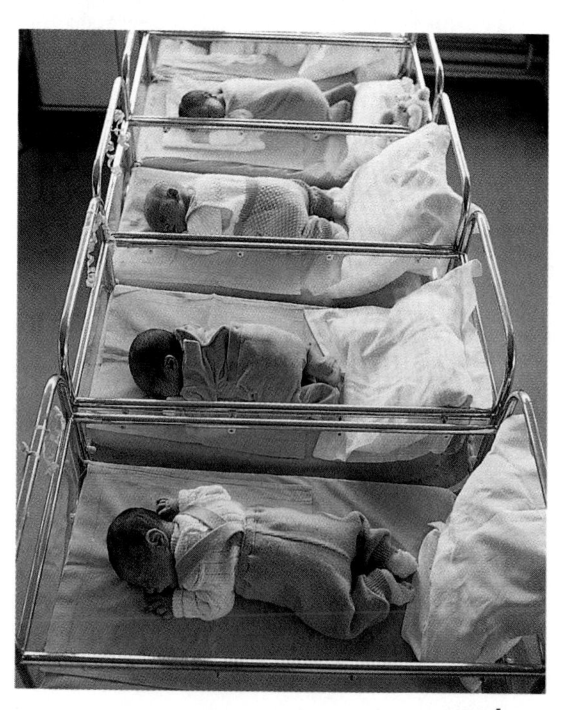

*newborn*

**nimble 1.** Light and quick in movement. The circus has *nimble* acrobats. **2.** Quick to understand or respond. In a debate, a *nimble* mind helps.
**nim•ble** (nim′bəl) *adjective,* **nimbler, nimblest.**

**nourish** To provide food needed for life and growth. Milk *nourishes* a baby or newborn animal.
**nour•ish** (nûr′ish) *verb,* **nourished, nourishing.**

# O

**observation 1.** The act or power of noticing. The detective's careful *observation* helped the police to solve the crime. **2.** Something said; comment; remark. I made an *observation* about the weather.
**ob•ser•va•tion** (ob′zər vā′shən) *noun, plural* **observations.**

**offend** To cause to be angry or unhappy. I'm sorry that my rude remark *offended* you.
**of•fend** (ə fend′) *verb,* **offended, offending.**

**Ojibway** Another spelling of **Ojibwa. 1.** A group of Native Americans formerly living in the Great Lakes region, now living mainly in Minnesota, Wisconsin, and North Dakota. **2.** A member of this group. **3.** The language of this group. *Also,* **Chippewa.**
**O•jib•way** (ō jib′wa) *noun, plural* **Ojibway** *or* **Ojibways.**

**ominous** Telling of trouble or bad luck to come; threatening.
**om•i•nous** (om′e nəs) *adjective.*

**onlooker** A person who looks on without taking part; spectator. I was only an *onlooker* while my sisters argued.
**on•look•er** (ôn′lůk′ər) *noun, plural* **onlookers.**

**ooze** To leak or pass out slowly through small holes or openings; seep.
**ooze** (üz) *verb,* **oozed, oozing.**

*ooze*

**ore** A mineral or rock that is mined for the metal or other substance it contains. ▲ Other words that sound like this are **oar** and **or.**
**ore** (ôr) *noun, plural* **ores.**

**organize 1.** To cause to join together in a labor union or other *organization.* **2.** To arrange or put together in an orderly way. Who is in charge of *organizing* the trip to the zoo?
**or•gan•ize** (ôr′gə nīz′) *verb,* **organized, organizing.**

**originate 1.** To bring into being; start. Who *originated* the design for this new airplane? **2.** To come into being; begin. The fire *originated* in an old, deserted building.
**o•rig•i•nate** (ə rij′ə nāt′) *verb,* **originated, originating.**

at; āpe; fär; câre; end; mē; it; īce; pîerce; hot; ōld; sông; fôrk; oil; out; up; ūse; rüle; půll; tûrn; chin; sing; shop; thin; this; hw in white; zh in treasure. The symbol ə stands for the unstressed vowel sound in about, taken, pencil, lemon, and circus.

**orphanage** A place that takes in and cares for children whose parents are dead.
**or•phan•age** (ôr′fə nij) *noun, plural* **orphanages.**

**overhang** To hang out over something; to jut out over. The trees *overhang* the street.
**o•ver•hang** (ō′vər hang′) *verb,* **overhung, overhanging.**

# P

**participate** To join with others; take part. Everyone *participated* in the rally.
**par•tic•i•pate** (pär tis′ə pāt′) *verb,* **participated, participating.**

**patio** A paved outdoor space for cooking, eating, and relaxing. Our neighbors dine on their *patio* every weekend.
**pa•ti•o** (pat′ē ō′) *noun, plural* **patios.**

**patriot** A person who loves his/her country and defends or supports it. We studied the lives of many American *patriots.*
**pa•tri•ot** (pā′trē ət) *noun, plural* **patriots.**

**pave** To cover a road or street with a hard surface. The workers were *paving* the street.
**pave** (pāv) *verb,* **paved, paving.**

**pavement** A hard covering or surface for a street, road, or sidewalk. A *pavement* is usually made from concrete or asphalt.
**pave•ment** (pāv′mənt) *noun, plural* **pavements.**

**payment** Money that is given to someone in return for things or work. *Payment* has to be made for the television set when it is delivered.
**pay•ment** (pā′mənt) *noun, plural* **payments.**

**peddler** A person who travels from place to place with goods for sale. I bought an apple for my lunch from a *peddler* on a street corner.
**ped•dler** (ped′lər) *noun, plural* **peddlers.**

*peddler*

**pelt**[1] To strike over and over again with small, hard things. The children *pelted* each other with snowballs.
**pelt** (pelt) *verb,* **pelted, pelting.**

**pelt**[2] The skin of an animal with its hair, fur, or wool. *Pelts* are used to make clothing and rugs.
**pelt** (pelt) *noun, plural* **pelts.**

**permission** A consent from someone in authority. You should ask your parents for *permission* to stay overnight at my house.
**per•mis•sion** (pər mish′ən) *noun.*

**persuade** To cause to do or believe something by pleading or giving reasons; convince. The principal *persuaded* the students to stop littering the school playground.
**per•suade** (pər swād′) *verb,* **persuaded, persuading.**

**pier 1.** A pillar or other kind of support that is used to hold up a bridge. Modern bridges have steel *piers* to support them. **2.** A structure built out over the water. It is used as a landing place for boats or ships. ▲ Another word that sounds like this is **peer.**
**pier** (pîr) *noun, plural* **piers.**

**potlatch** A feast held by some Native American tribes of the Pacific Northwest at which the host gives away and sometimes destroys valuable objects as a sign of wealth, and to establish his social status.
**pot•latch** (pot'lach') *noun.*

**poverty** A lack of money; the condition of being poor. That family lives in *poverty.*
**pov•er•ty** (pov'ər tē) *noun.*

**prehistoric** Belonging to a time before people started writing history. Dinosaurs were *prehistoric* animals.
**pre•his•tor•ic** (prē'his tôr'ik) *adjective.*

**presence 1.** The fact of being in a place at a certain time. The *presence* of the growling dog in the room made me nervous. **2.** The area around or near a person. The document had to be signed in the *presence* of a witness.
**pres•ence** (prez'əns) *noun.*

**previous** Coming before; earlier. We were introduced at the *previous* meeting.
**pre•vi•ous** (prē'vē əs) *adjective.*

**probe** To investigate or explore thoroughly. The police *probed* the details of the bank's dishonest practices. *Verb.*
—A tool or device used to test or explore. A doctor might use a *probe* to look into an injured ear. *Noun.*
**probe** (prōb) *noun, plural* **probes;** *verb,* **probed, probing.**

**prologue** An introduction to a play, poem, story, or other literary work.
**pro•logue** (prō'lôg *or* prō'log) *noun, plural* **prologues.**

**Word History**

The word **prologue** comes from the Latin word *prologus,* which means "preface to a play." *Prologus* can be traced back to the Greek *pro-,* meaning "before," and *legein,* meaning "to speak." The Greek word for "something that is spoken before" took on the meaning of "introduction."

**prospector** A person who explores for gold or other minerals.
**pros•pec•tor** (pros'pek tər) *noun, plural* **prospectors.**

*prospector*

at; āpe; fär; câre; end; mē; it; īce; pîerce; hot; ōld; sông; fôrk; oil; out; up; ūse; rüle; pu̇ll; tûrn; chin; sing; shop; thin; this; hw in white; zh in treasure. The symbol ə stands for the unstressed vowel sound in about, taken, pencil, lemon, and circus.

**publicity** **1.** The attention of the public. Most politicians like *publicity.* **2.** Information given out to bring a person or thing to the attention of the public. The *publicity* about the singers brought a large crowd to see them.
**pub•lic•i•ty** (pub lis′i tē) *noun.*

# Q

**quench** **1.** To put an end to by satisfying. I *quenched* my thirst with a long drink of water. **2.** To make something stop burning; put out; extinguish. I *quenched* the fire.
**quench** (kwench) *verb,* **quenched, quenching.**

# R

**rascal** **1.** A mischievous person or animal. That pup is a *rascal.* **2.** A dishonest person; rogue.
**ras•cal** (ras′kəl) *noun, plural* **rascals.**

**rasp** To make a harsh, grating sound. The iron gate *rasped* because the hinges were rusty.
**rasp** (rasp) *verb,* **rasped, rasping.**

**reaction** An action in response to something that has happened or has been done. What was your parents' *reaction* when they saw your report card?
**re•ac•tion** (rē ak′shən) *noun, plural* **reactions.**

**reasonable** **1.** Showing or using good sense and thinking; not foolish. A *reasonable* person will always listen to both sides of an argument. **2.** Not too expensive. The grocery store's prices are *reasonable.*
**rea•son•a•ble** (rē′zə nə bəl) *adjective*

**recital** **1.** A performance or concert of music or dance. We went to a piano *recital* in the auditorium. **2.** A story or account. Your *recital* of your experiences in Africa was fascinating.
**re•cit•al** (ri sī′təl) *noun, plural* **recitals.**

*recital*

**reduce** **1.** To make or become less or smaller in size, number, or degree. Drivers should *reduce* their speed if the road is slippery. **2.** To bring to a lesser form, condition, or position. The forest was *reduced* to ashes by the fire.
**re•duce** (ri düs′) *verb,* **reduced, reducing.**

**reef** A ridge of sand, rock, or coral that lies at or near the surface of the ocean or another body of water. If you go scuba diving near a coral *reef* you will see a wide variety of marine animals.
**reef** (rēf) *noun, plural* **reefs.**

**register** To have one's name placed on a list or record. Voters must *register* before they can vote. *Verb.*
—**1.** An official list or record or a book used for this. Guests signed the hotel *register.* **2.** A machine that automatically records and counts. A cash *register* records money it takes in. *Noun.*
**reg•is•ter** (rej'ə stər) *noun, plural* **registers;** *verb,* **registered, registering.**

**regret** To feel sorry about. I *regret* having said unkind things to my friends.
**re•gret** (ri gret') *verb,* **regretted, regretting.**

**reject** To refuse to accept, allow, or approve. The voters *rejected* the tax plan.
**re•ject** (ri jekt') *verb,* **rejected, rejecting.**

**reliable** Able to be depended on and trusted. That worker is a *reliable* person who finishes every job on time.
**re•li•a•ble** (ri lī'ə bəl) *adjective.*

**relieve** **1.** To free from discomfort or pain; comfort, help, or aid. I took medicine to *relieve* my cough. **2.** To free from a job or duty. The nurses stayed on duty until they were *relieved.*
**re•lieve** (ri lēv') *verb,* **relieved, relieving.**

**reluctantly** Unwillingly. She *reluctantly* got into the airplane even though she is afraid of heights.
**re•luc•tant•ly** (ri luk'tənt lē) *adverb.*

**reptile** One of a class of cold-blooded animals with a backbone. Reptiles have dry, scaly skin. They move by crawling on their stomachs or creeping on short legs. Lizards, snakes, alligators, and turtles are *reptiles.*
**rep•tile** (rep'təl *or* rep'tīl) *noun, plural* **reptiles.**

*reptiles*

**reserve** **1.** To arrange to have something kept for a particular person or purpose. My parents *reserved* rooms in a hotel. **2.** To keep for oneself. I *reserve* the right to make up my own mind.
**re•serve** (ri zûrv') *verb,* **reserved, reserving.**

**restless** **1.** Not able to rest. We got *restless* because the speech was so long. **2.** Not giving rest. The patient spent a *restless* night.
**rest•less** (rest'lis) *adjective.*

at; āpe; fär; câre; end; mē; it; īce; pîerce; hot; ōld; sông; fôrk; oil; out; up; ūse; rüle; pu̇ll; tûrn; chin; sing; shop; thin; th̲is; hw in white; zh in treasure. The symbol ə stands for the unstressed vowel sound in about, taken, pencil, lemon, and circus.

**restore** **1.** To bring back to a former or original state or condition. The old house has been *restored* by its new owners. **2.** To give or put back. The police *restored* the bicycle to its owner.
**re•store** (ri stôr′) *verb,* **restored, restoring.**

**reveal** **1.** To make known. Don't *reveal* my secret. **2.** To show; display. The magician opened the lid to *reveal* a bunny.
**re•veal** (ri vēl′) *verb,* **revealed, revealing.**

**rival** A person who is, or tries to be, as good as or better than another. The two students were *rivals* for class president.
**ri•val** (rī′vəl) *noun, plural* **rivals.**

**Rocky Mountains** A group of mountain ranges reaching from New Mexico to Alaska
**Rock•y Moun•tains** (rok′ē moun′tənz) *noun.*

**rowdy** Rude; boisterous; disorderly. The police were called when the crowd became *rowdy.*
**row•dy** (rou′dē) *adjective.*

**ruby** A clear, red precious stone.
**ru•by** (rü′bē) *noun, plural* **rubies.**

# S

**sacred** **1.** Belonging to a god; having to do with religion. Our choir sings *sacred* music. **2.** Deserving to be treated with great respect. The memory of the dead hero was *sacred* to the town.
**sa•cred** (sā′krid) *adjective.*

**scheme** **1.** A plan or plot for doing something. The crooks had a *scheme* for robbing the bank. **2.** An orderly arrangement of related things; design. You can choose the color *scheme* for your room.
**scheme** (skēm) *noun, plural* **schemes.**

**scratch** *Idiom.* **from scratch.** From the beginning; with no resources. When their business failed, they had to start again *from scratch.*
**scratch** (skrach) *noun.*

**Second Congressional District** One of the divisions of a state that elects a member of the House of Representatives.
**Sec•ond Con•gres•sion•al Dis•trict** (sek′ənd kən gresh′ə nəl dis′trikt) *noun.*

**shack** A small, roughly built hut or cabin.
**shack** (shak) *noun, plural* **shacks.**

**shaky** **1.** Trembling; shaking. The frightened person answered in a *shaky* voice. **2.** Not firm; unsound. The old bridge is *shaky.*
**shak•y** (shā′kē) *adjective,* **shakier, shakiest.**

**shoreline** The outline or contour of the land along the edge of an ocean, lake, or large river.
**shore•line** (shôr′līn′) *noun, plural* **shorelines.**

*shoreline*

**shrivel** To shrink, wrinkle, or wither. The plant *shriveled* in the heat.
**shriv•el** (shriv′əl) *verb,* **shriveled, shriveling.**

**silverware** Spoons, forks, dishes, or anything else for the table that is made of or coated with silver.
**sil•ver•ware** (sil′vər wâr′) *noun.*

**Sioux** Another word for **Dakota.** **1.** Any of several groups of Native Americans that once spoke similar languages, and formerly lived on the Great Plains. **2.** A member of one of these groups. **3.** The language of one of these groups.
**Sioux** (sü) *noun, plural* **Sioux** (sü, süz).

**skeptical** Having or showing doubt or disbelief.
**skep•ti•cal** (skep′ti kəl) *adjective.*

**sliver** A thin, often pointed piece that has been broken, cut, or torn off; splinter. I got a *sliver* of wood in my toe. I'd like a *sliver* of pie.
**sliv•er** (sliv′ər) *noun, plural* **slivers.**

**smear** To spread something wet, sticky, or greasy on something else.
**smear** (smîr) *verb,* **smeared, smearing.**

**souvenir** Something that is kept because it reminds one of a person, place, or event.
**sou•ve•nir** (sü′və nîr′ *or* sü′v nîr′) *noun, plural* **souvenirs.**

**species** A group of animals or plants that have many characteristics in common. Poodles and beagles belong to the same *species.*
**spe•cies** (spē′shēz) *noun, plural.*

**specimen** A single person or thing that shows what the whole group is like; sample. I collect *specimens* of different kinds of butterflies.
**spec•i•men** (spes′ə mən) *noun, plural* **specimens.**

**speechless** Not able to say anything. You were *speechless* when we yelled "Surprise!"
**speech•less** (spēch′lis) *adjective.*

**stained** Having marks or spots. The rug was *stained* where the ink spilled on it.
**stained** (stānd) *adjective.*

**stallion** An adult male horse.
**stal•lion** (stal′yən) *noun, plural* **stallions.**

*stallion*

**starvation** The act or state of suffering or dying of hunger.
**star•va•tion** (stär vā′shən) *noun.*

**static electricity** A quantity of electricity that builds up on an object and does not flow away. *Static electricity* can be created by combing dry hair with a dry comb.
**stat•ic e•lec•tric•i•ty** (stat′ik i lek tris′ i tē) *noun.*

**a**t; **ā**pe; f**ä**r; c**â**re; **e**nd; m**ē**; **i**t; **ī**ce; p**î**erce; h**o**t; **ō**ld; s**ô**ng; f**ô**rk; **oi**l; **ou**t; **u**p; **ū**se; r**ü**le; p**u̇**ll; t**û**rn; **ch**in; si**ng**; **sh**op; **th**in; **th**is; **hw** in **wh**ite; **zh** in trea**s**ure. The symbol **ə** stands for the unstressed vowel sound in **a**bout, tak**e**n, penc**i**l, lem**o**n, and circ**u**s.

**stern** The rear part of a boat or ship.
**stern** (stûrn) *noun, plural* **sterns.**

*stern*

**stifle** 1. To make breathing difficult for; smother. The smoke *stifled* the people in the burning building. **2.** To be unable to breath normally; feel smothered. I opened the windows because I was *stifling.* **3.** To hold back; stop. I *stifled* a yawn.
**sti•fle** (stī'fəl) *verb,* **stifled, stifling.**

**stride** To walk with long steps. We watched the models *stride* in their fancy clothes. *Verb.*
—**1.** A long step. My friend has a quick *stride.* **2.** Progress or improvement. Science has made *strides* in fighting disease. *Noun.*
**stride** (strīd) *noun, plural* **strides;** *verb,* **strode, stridden, striding.**

**stun 1.** To shock. We were *stunned* by the news. **2.** To make unconscious. The robin was *stunned* when it flew into the window.
**stun** (stun) *verb,* **stunned, stunning.**

**submit 1.** To present. Please *submit* your book reports on Monday. **2.** To yield to some power or authority. The children *submitted* to their parents' wishes.
**sub•mit** (səb mit') *verb,* **submitted, submitting.**

**subterranean** Being, located, or happening below the surface of the earth; underground. The train carries passengers through a *subterranean* tunnel.
**sub•ter•ra•ne•an** (sub'tə ra'ne ən) *adjective.*

**summon 1.** To ask to come. We *summoned* the police to the car accident. **2.** To stir up; arouse. I *summoned* my courage and dove off the high diving board.
**sum•mon** (sum'ən) *verb,* **summoned, summoning.**

**survey 1.** To look at or study in detail. The mayor *surveyed* the damage to the city after the storm. **2.** To measure land to fix or find out its boundaries. They *surveyed* the property before it was divided into lots.
**sur•vey** (sər vā') *verb,* **surveyed, surveying.**

**swerve** To turn aside suddenly. The driver *swerved* to avoid hitting the dog.
**swerve** (swûrv) *verb,* **swerved, swerving.**

**swollen** Made larger by swelling. I can't get my ring on my *swollen* finger.
**swol•len** (swo'lən) *adjective.*

# T

**Tahcawin** (täk'shô we ä).

**tantie** In Trinidad, a female relative who assists in the upbringing of young children.
**tan•tie** (tän tē) *noun.*

**Tasinagi** (tä'she nä ge).

**technique** A method or way of bringing about a desired result in a science, art, sport, or profession. The farmer taught me some good *techniques* for planting crops.
**tech•nique** (tek nēk′) *noun, plural* **techniques.**

**temporary** Lasting or used for a short time only. Some students try to find *temporary* jobs for the summer.
**tem•po•rar•y** (tem′pə rer′ē) *adjective.*

**thief** A person who steals. The *thief* broke into the house and stole the television.
**thief** (thēf) *noun, plural* **thieves.**

**threat** A person or thing that might cause harm; danger. The outbreak of flu was a *threat* to everyone in the community.
**threat** (thret) *noun, plural* **threats.**

**thrive** To be successful; do well. This plant *thrives* in the sun.
**thrive** (thrīv) *verb,* **thrived, thriving.**

**Tonweya** (ton wa′yə).

**transatlantic** Crossing or spanning the Atlantic Ocean. I made a *transatlantic* telephone call.
**trans•at•lan•tic** (trans′ət lan′tik *or* tranz′ət lan′tik) *adjective.*

**treacherous** Full of danger; hazardous. Many ships have sunk in those *treacherous* waters.
**treach•er•ous** (trech′ər əs) *adjective.*

**treatment** **1.** The care or medicine used to help cure a sick or injured person. Rest was the recommended *treatment.* **2.** The way something or someone is treated. That scratched record has had rough *treatment.*
**treat•ment** (trēt′mənt) *noun, plural* **treatments.**

**tropical** Having to do with or found in the region of the earth that is near the equator. Most monkeys live in *tropical* forests.
**trop•i•cal** (trop′i kəl) *adjective.*

*tropical*

**tutor** A teacher who gives private lessons to a pupil.
**tu•tor** (tü′tər *or* tū′tər) *noun, plural* **tutors.**

**Word History**

The word **tutor** comes from the Latin word *tutor,* meaning "defender" or "guardian." In some English universities, the word *tutor* was used for a graduate responsible for a younger student. From this meaning came the sense of "a private teacher."

**at**; **ā**pe; f**ä**r; c**â**re; **e**nd; m**ē**; **i**t; **ī**ce; p**î**erce; h**o**t; **ō**ld; s**ô**ng; f**ô**rk; **oi**l; **ou**t; **u**p; **ū**se; r**ü**le; p**ù**ll; t**û**rn; **ch**in; si**ng**; **sh**op; **th**in; **th**is; **hw** in **wh**ite; **zh** in trea**s**ure. The symbol **ə** stands for the unstressed vowel sound in **a**bout, tak**e**n, penc**i**l, lem**o**n, and circ**u**s.

**typical** Showing the qualities or characteristics of a certain type. A *typical* movie lasts about ninety minutes.
**typ•i•cal** (tip'i kəl) *adjective.*

**Tyrannosaurus Rex** A huge dinosaur that lived in North America in prehistoric times.
**ty•ran•no•sau•rus rex** (ti ran'ə sôr'əs reks) *noun.*

*Tyrannosaurus Rex*

# U

**universe** Everything that exists, including Earth, the planets, the stars, and all of space.
**u•ni•verse** (ū'nə vûrs') *noun.*

> **Word History**
>
> The word **universe** comes from a Latin word that means "the whole world."

# V

**vaguely** In a way that is not clear or definite. I only *vaguely* know how to get to the theater.
**vaguely** (vāg'lē) *adverb.*

**vandalize** To damage or destroy property willfully.
**van•dal•ize** (van'də līz') *verb,* **vandalized, vandalizing.**

> **Word History**
>
> The word **vandalize** comes from *Vandals,* the name of a group of people who lived in northern Europe more than 1,500 years ago. In the fourth and fifth centuries A.D., the *Vandals* made destructive raids into the areas that are now France, Spain, and Italy. Today, *vandalize* means "to destroy property, especially something of artistic or religious value." A person who vandalizes is called a *vandal.*

**vaporize** To change or be changed into small particles of mist, steam, or smoke that can be seen in the air. When water boils in a pot, it *vaporizes* into the air.
**va•por•ize** (vā'pə rīz') *verb,* **vaporized, vaporizing.**

**variety** A number of different things. We bought a *variety* of foods at the grocery store.
**va•ri•e•ty** (və rī'i tē) *noun, plural* **varieties.**

**visible** Able to be seen. Their house is *visible* from the road.
**vis•i•ble** (viz e bel) *adjective.*

# W

**Waŋbli** The word for "eagle" in the language of the Lakota people.
**Waŋ•bli** (wäm ble′) *noun.*

**wampum** Small, polished beads made from shells and strung together or woven into belts, collars, and necklaces. *Wampum* was used by some Native Americans as money.
**wam•pum** (wom′pəm) *or* (wôm′pəm) *noun.*

*wampum*

**wedge** A piece of wood, metal, plastic, or other substance that is thick at one end and narrow at the other. We served a *wedge* of cheese with some crackers.
**wedge** (wej) *noun, plural* **wedges.**

**whist** A card game for two pairs of players, played with a full deck of fifty-two cards.
**whist** (hwist *or* wist) *noun.*

# Y

**Yukon** A territory in northwestern Canada that borders Alaska.
**Yu•kon** (ū′kon) *noun.*

# Z

**zooxanthella** A very small, single-celled organism with two whiplike "tails."
**zo•o•xan•thel•la** (zo′ə zan thel′ə) *noun, plural* **zooxanthellae.**

**Word History**

The word **zooxanthella** comes from the Greek words *zoe,* meaning "life," and *xanthos,* meaning "yellow," and the Latin word ending *-ella,* meaning "small." Literally, then, *zooxanthella* means "a small, yellow living thing."

**a**t; **ā**pe; f**ä**r; c**â**re; **e**nd; m**ē**; **i**t; **ī**ce; p**î**erce; h**o**t; **ō**ld; s**ô**ng; f**ô**rk; **oi**l; **ou**t; **u**p; **ū**se; r**ü**le; p**u̇**ll; t**û**rn; **ch**in; si**ng**; **sh**op; **th**in; **th**is; **hw** in **wh**ite; **zh** in trea**s**ure. The symbol **ə** stands for the unstressed vowel sound in **a**bout, tak**e**n, penc**i**l, lem**o**n, and circ**u**s.

## ACKNOWLEDGMENTS

*The publisher gratefully acknowledges permission to reprint the following copyrighted material:*

"The Act" from WILLIAM CARLOS WILLIAMS: COLLECTED POEMS 1939-1962, Volume II. Copyright © 1948 by William Carlos Williams. Reprinted by permission of New Directions Publishing Corp.

"Amazing...But True! Bridges" from AMAZING...BUT TRUE! BRIDGES AND TUNNELS by Laura Allen. SUPERSCIENCE BLUE, January 1995, Volume 6, Number 4, Copyright © 1995 by Scholastic. Reprinted by permission.

"Ben and Me" from BEN AND ME by Robert Lawson. Copyright 1939 by Robert Lawson; © renewed 1967 by John W. Boyd. By permission of Little, Brown and Company.

"The Best Bad Thing" from THE BEST BAD THING by Yoshiko Uchida. Copyright © 1983 by Yoshiko Uchida. Reprinted with permission of Margaret K. McElderry Books, an imprint of Simon & Schuster Books for Young Readers.

Cover use of THE BEST BAD THING, THE HAPPIEST ENDING, and A JAR OF DREAMS all by Yoshiko Uchida. Covers by Kinuko Craft and used with permission of the artist.

Cover permission for THE BIG ROCK by Bruce Hiscock. Copyright © 1988 by Atheneum. Reprinted by permission.

"The Big Storm" by Bruce Hiscock. Copyright © 1993 by Bruce Hiscock. Published by Atheneum. Reprinted by permission.

"Breaker's Bridge" from THE RAINBOW PEOPLE by Laurence Yep. Text copyright © 1989 by Laurence Yep. Reprinted by permission of HarperCollins Publisher.

"Calvin and Hobbes" from THE ESSENTIAL CALVIN AND HOBBES: A CALVIN AND HOBBES TREASURY by Bill Watterson. Copyright © 1988 by Bill Watterson. Published by Andrews and McMeel Books. Reprinted by permission.

"Change" from RIVER WINDING by Charlotte Zolotow. Copyright © 1970 by Charlotte Zolotow. Reprinted by permission by HarperCollins Publishers.

Book covers for CHRONICLES OF NARNIA by C. S. Lewis. Reproduced with the permission of the Macmillan Publishing Company.

"City" reprinted by permission of Harold Ober Associates, Incorporated. Copyright © 1958 by Langston Hughes. Renewed 1986 by George Houston Bass.

"Como un recuerdo/Like a Memory" from JUNTO AL ALAMO DE LOS SINSONTES by Emilio de Armas. Copyright © 1988 Ediciones Casa de las Americas. Published by Ediciones Casa de las Americas. Reprinted by permission.

"Crystal Rowe" from CLASS DISMISSED II by Mel Glenn. Copyright © 1986 by Mel Glenn. Published by Clarion Books/Ticknor & Fields, a Houghton Mifflin Company. Reprinted by permission.

"Curious Ben" from KIDS DISCOVER magazine, Volume 4, Issue 9, November 1994. Copyright © 1994 by Kids Discover Magazine. Reprinted by permission.

"Dear Mr. Henshaw" from DEAR MR. HENSHAW by Beverly Cleary. Copyright © 1983 by Beverly Cleary. Used by permission of William Morrow & Company, Inc., Publishers, New York.

"The Diary of Martha Baker Wilson" from ALASKA GOLD RUSH DIARY OF MARTHA BAKER WILSON by Grace Esterbrook Fake. Copyright © 1982 by Grace E. Fake.

"Dive to the Coral Reefs" from DIVE TO THE CORAL REEFS: A NEW ENGLAND AQUARIUM BOOK written by Elizabeth Tayntor, Paul Erickson, and Les Kaufman. Copyright © 1986 by the New England Aquarium. Reprinted by permission of Crown Publishers, Inc. Permission also from Mews Books Ltd. for New England Aquarium.

"For Poets" by Al Young. Copyright © 1968 by Al Young. Reprinted with permission of the author.

"For Purple Mountains' Majesty" from THE MALIBU AND OTHER POEMS by Myra Cohn Livingston. Copyright © 1972 by Myra Cohn Livingston. Reprinted by permission of Marian Reiner for the author.

"Fossils" reprinted with permission of Atheneum Books for Young Readers, an imprint of Simon & Schuster Children's Publishing Division, 1969. Simon & Schuster from SOMETHING NEW BEGINS by Lilian Moore. Copyright © 1982 by Lilian Moore.

Book cover for THE GARDEN OF ABDUL GASAZI by Chris Van Allsburg. Copyright © 1979 by Chris Van Allsburg. Reprinted by permission of Houghton Mifflin Co. All rights reserved.

"The Gold Coin" from THE GOLD COIN by Alma Flor Ada. Copyright © 1991 by Alma Flor Ada. Illustrations copyright © 1991 by Neil Waldman. Reprinted with permission from Atheneum Books for Young Readers, an imprint of Simon & Schuster Children's Publishing Division.

"Grandma Essie's Covered Wagon" by David Williams, illustrated by Wiktor Sadowski. Text copyright © 1993 by David Williams. Illustrations copyright © 1993 by Wiktor Sadowski. Reprinted by permission.

Jacket illustration from the Avon Books edition of HENRY AND BEEZUS by Beverly Cleary, illustrated by Frederika Ribes. Text copyright © 1952 by Beverly Cleary. Reprinted by permission of William Morrow and Company, Inc.

"How It Feels to Fight for Your Life" from HOW IT FEELS TO FIGHT FOR YOUR LIFE by Jill Krementz. Copyright © 1989, 1991 by Jill Krementz, Inc. Reprinted by permission of Little, Brown and Company.

Book cover for HOW IT FEELS WHEN A PARENT DIES by Jill Krementz. Copyright © 1981 by Jill Krementz. Reprinted by permission of Alfred A. Knopf, Inc.

"How to Think Like a Scientist" from HOW TO THINK LIKE A SCIENTIST: ANSWERING QUESTIONS BY THE SCIENTIFIC METHOD by Stephen P. Kramer. Copyright © 1987 by Stephen P. Kramer. Reprinted by permission of HarperCollins Publishers.

"Human-Made Reef Relief" reprint permission and copyright © 1994 by Weekly Reader Corporation. All Rights Reserved.

"I Love the Look of Words" by Maya Angelou, copyright © 1993 by Maya Angelou, from SOUL LOOKS BACK IN WONDER by Tom Feelings. Used by permission of Dial Books for Young Readers, a division of Penguin Books USA Inc.

"Identified Flying Objects" by Margaret McKelway from NATIONAL GEOGRAPHIC WORLD, Number 239, July 1995. Copyright © 1995 by the National Geographic Society. Reprinted by permission.

"The Impossible Trick" from EINSTEIN ANDERSON MAKES UP FOR LOST TIME by Seymour Simon. Copyright © 1981 by Seymour Simon. Used by permission of Viking Penguin, a division of Penguin USA, Inc.

"The Incredible Shrinking Machine" from EINSTEIN ANDERSON, SCIENCE SLEUTH by Seymour Simon. Copyright © 1980 by Seymour Simon. Used by permission of Viking Penguin Books USA, Inc.

"It's Our World, Too!" from IT'S OUR WORLD TOO! by Phillip Hoose. Copyright © 1993 by Phillip Hoose. By permission of Little, Brown and Company.

"Jigsaw Puzzle" by Russell Hoban reprinted by permission of Harold Ober Associates, Incorporated. Copyright © 1970 by Russell Hoban.

Book cover for JUMANJI by Chris Van Allsburg. Copyright © 1981 by Chris Van Allsburg. Reprinted by permission of Houghton Mifflin Co. All rights reserved.

"Klondike Fever" from GOLD! THE KLONDIKE ADVENTURE by Delia Ray. Copyright © 1989 by Laing Communications, Inc. Used by permission of Lodestar Books, an affiliate of Dutton Children's Books, a division of Penguin USA, Inc.

"Knoxville, Tennessee" from BLACK FEELINGS, BLACK TALK, BLACK JUDGEMENT by Nikki Giovanni. Copyright © 1968, 1970 by Nikki Giovanni. Published by William Morrow and Company. Reprinted by permission.

"maggie and milly and molly and may" is reprinted from COMPLETE POEMS: 1904-1962 by e. e. cummings, Edited by George J. Firmage, by permission of Liveright Publishing Corporation. Copyright © 1956, 1984, 1991 by the Trustees for the E. E. Cummings Trust.

"Magnet" from MORE SMALL POEMS by Valerie Worth. Copyright © 1976 by Valerie Worth. Published by Farrar, Straus & Giroux, Inc. Reprinted by permission.

"Making a Difference" by Tracy Williams Cheney and Connie Eden from FALCON MAGAZINE, Volume 3, Number 4, July/August 1995. Copyright © 1995 by Falcon Press Publishing. Reprinted by permission.

"The Marble Champ" from BASEBALL IN APRIL AND OTHER STORIES, copyright © 1990 by Gary Soto. Reprinted by permission of Harcourt Brace & Company.

"Money, Money, Money" from SPIDER Magazine January 1995 Volume 2, Number 1. Copyright © 1995 by Carus Publishing Co.

Book cover for MR. REVERE AND I by Robert Lawson. Copyright 1953 by Robert Lawson. Copyright © renewed by John W. Boyd. By permission of Little, Brown and Company.

"My Adventures at the Center of the Earth" by Ana Maria Shua. Copyright © 1988 by Editorial Sudamericana. Reprinted by permission.

"My Floor Is Somebody's Ceiling" from THE BUTTERFLY JAR by Jeff Moss. Copyright © 1989 by Jeff Moss. Used by permission of Bantam Books, a division of Bantam Doubleday Dell Publishing Group, Inc.

"my friend" by Emily Hearn from HOCKEY CARDS AND HOPSCOTCH by John McInnes & Emily Hearn. Copyright © 1971. Used with permission of Nelson Canada, a Division of Thomson Canada Limited.

"New Providence" from NEW PROVIDENCE: A CHANGING CITYSCAPE by Renata Von Tscharner and Ronald Lee Fleming, The Townscape Institute, illustrations by Denis Orloff. Text copyright © 1987 by Renata Von Tscharner and Ronald Lee Fleming, The Townscape Institute, Inc. Illustrations copyright © 1987 by The Townscape Institute, Inc. and Denis Orloff. Reprinted and reproduced by permission of Harcourt Brace Jovanovich, Inc.

"The News About Dinosaurs" reprinted with the permission of Simon & Schuster Books for Young Readers from THE NEWS ABOUT DINOSAURS by Patricia Lauber. Copyright © 1989 Patricia Lauber.

"The Old Walking Song" (credited as "The Road Goes Ever On and On...") from THE FELLOWSHIP OF THE RING by J. R. R. Tolkien. Copyright © 1965 by J. R. R. Tolkien. Reprinted by permission of Houghton Mifflin Company. By permission also of Unwin Hyman, an imprint of HarperCollins Publishers Limited.

"A Path to the Moon" from GIANT MOONQUAKES AND OTHER DISASTERS by b p Nichol. Reprinted by permission of Black Moss Press.

"Peanuts" by Charles Schulz. Copyright © 1979 by United Feature Syndicate, Inc.

Book cover for RABBIT HILL by Robert Lawson. Copyright 1944 by Robert Lawson. Renewed copyright © 1971 John W. Boyd. Used by permission of Viking Penguin, a division of Penguin Books USA Inc.

"Scuba Diving" from THE RAGGED HEART by Stuart Francis. Copyright © 1989 by Stuart Francis and used with his permission.

"Secret Talk" from A WORD OR TWO WITH YOU by Eve Merriam. Copyright © 1981 by Eve Merriam. Used by permission of Marian Reiner for the author.

"The Silent Lobby" by Mildred Pitts Walter from THE BIG BOOK FOR PEACE edited by Ann Durrell and Marilyn Sachs. Copyright © 1990 by Mildred Pitts Walter.

"A Song of Greatness" from CHILDREN SING IN THE FAR WEST by Mary Austin. Copyright © 1928 by Mary Austin. Copyright © renewed 1956 by Kenneth M. Chapman and Mary C. Wheelwright. Reprinted by permission of Houghton Mifflin Company.

"Stopping by Woods on a Snowy Evening" from THE POETRY OF ROBERT FROST, edited by Edward Connery Lathem. Copyright 1951 by Robert Frost. Copyright 1923 © 1969 by Henry Holt and Co., Inc. Reprinted by permission of Henry Holt and Co., Inc.

"The Talking Eggs" from THE TALKING EGGS by Robert D. San Souci, pictures by Jerry Pinkney. Copyright © 1989 by Robert D. San Souci, text. Copyright © 1989 by Jerry Pinkney, pictures. Used by permission of Dial Books for Young Readers, a division of Penguin Books USA Inc.

Book cover for THEY WERE STRONG AND GOOD by Robert Lawson. Copyright 1940 by Robert Lawson, renewed © 1968 by John W. Boyd. Used by permission of Viking Penguin, a division of Penguin Books USA Inc.

"Three" by Elizabeth Coatsworth reprinted by permission of Grosset & Dunlap, Inc. from THE SPARROW BUSH by Elizabeth Coatsworth, copyright © 1966, 1994 by Grosset & Dunlap, Inc.

"Tired of Giving In" Adapted from AMERICAN GIRL, Vol. 2, number 5. © 1994 by Pleasant Company. Reprinted by permission of Pleasant Company.

"To Catch a Fish" from UNDER THE SUNDAY TREE by Eloise Greenfield. Paintings by Mr. Amos Ferguson. Text copyright © 1988 by Eloise Greenfield. Painting copyright © 1988 by Mr. Amos Furguson. Reprinted by permission.

"Tonweya and the Eagles" from TONWEYA AND THE EAGLES by Rosebud Yellow Robe, illustrated by Jerry Pinkney. Copyright © 1979 by Rosebud Yellow Rose Frantz, text. Copyright © 1979 by Jerry Pinkney, illustrations. Used by permission of Viking Penguin, a division of Penguin Books USA Inc.

Book cover for A VERY YOUNG DANCER by Jill Krementz. Copyright © 1976 by Jill Krementz. Reprinted by permission of Alfred A. Knopf, Inc.

"The Voyage of the Dawn Treader" from THE VOYAGE OF THE DAWN TREADER by C. S. Lewis. Reprinted by permission of HarperCollins Publishers.

Book cover for WALKING TO THE CREEK by David Williams, illustrated by Thomas B. Allen. Copyright © 1990 by Alfred A. Knopf. Reprinted by permission.

"A Wave in Her Pocket" from A WAVE IN HER POCKET: STORIES FROM TRINIDAD by Lynn Joseph. Text copyright © 1991 by Lynn Joseph. Reprinted by permission of Houghton Mifflin Company.

"What Is...the Sun?" by Wes Magee from THE WITCH'S BREW AND OTHER POEMS by Wes Magee. Copyright © 1989 Cambridge University Press, 1989.

"Who Am I?" from AT THE TOP OF MY VOICE AND OTHER POEMS by Felice Holman. Charles Scribner's Sons, © 1970. Permission of Felice Holman, copyright owner.

"Willie Bea and the Time the Martians Landed" from WILLIE BEA AND THE TIME THE MARTIANS LANDED by Virginia Hamilton. Copyright © 1983 by Virgina Hamilton. Used by permission of William Morrow and Company, Inc., Publishers, New York.

"Wouldn't You?" from YOU READ TO ME, I'LL READ TO YOU by John Ciardi. Copyright © 1962 by John Ciardi. Published by J. B. Lippincott. Reprinted by permission.

"The Wreck of the Zephyr" from THE WRECK OF THE ZEPHYR by Chris Van Allsburg. Copyright © 1983 by Chris Van Allsburg. Reprinted by permission of Houghton Mifflin Company. All rights reserved.

**READING RESOURCES**

Almanac: Reprinted with permission from The World Almanac and Book of Facts 1995. Copyright © 1994 Funk & Wagnalls Corporation. All rights reserved.

Dictionary: Excerpt from MACMILLAN SCHOOL DICTIONARY 1, copyright © 1991 by Macmillan/McGraw-Hill School Publishing Company. Reprinted by permission of Macmillan/McGraw-Hill School Publishing Company. Excerpt from THE NEW OXFORD PICTURE DICTIONARY, English/Spanish edition, edited by E.C. Parnwell. Copyright © 1989 by Oxford University Press. Reprinted by permission of Oxford University Press, Inc.

Index: From LIFE ON A CORAL REEF by Lionel Bender, copyright © 1989 by Gloucester Press. Reprinted by permission of Gloucester Press.

Maps: "United States: Climate" and "The United States: Landforms" from UNITED STATES AND ITS NEIGHBORS, copyright © 1991 by Macmillan/McGraw-Hill School Publishing Company. Reprinted by permission of Macmillan/McGraw-Hill School Publishing Company.

**COVER DESIGN:** Carbone Smolan Associates
**COVER ILLUSTRATION:** Robert M. Sullivan

**DESIGN CREDITS**
Carbone Smolan Associates, front matter, 118-119
Bill Smith Studio, 136-137, 180-183
Function Thru Form, Inc., 210-211, 216-217
Sheldon Cotler + Associates Editorial Group, 140-179, 208-209
Notovitz Design Inc., 212-215

**ILLUSTRATION CREDITS**
Robert M. Sullivan, 118-119; Robert Roper, 120-135; Sherry Bringham, 120-135, 185 (calligraphy); Carrie Hamilton, 136-137; Karen Jones Lee, 138-139; Chuck Schmidt, 180 (title); Kieth Witmer, 180-183 (borders); Young Sook Cho, 184-185 (bkgd.). **Reading Resources:** Matt Straub, 210-211. **Glossary:** Lori Anzalone, G3, G5, G12, G15, G17, G21, G23, G26; Greg King, G12; Bob Pepper, G19.

**PHOTOGRAPHY CREDITS**
All photographs are by the Macmillan/McGraw-Hill School Division (MMSD) except as noted below.

136-137: 147: b. Jonathan Blair/National Geographic Society Image Collection. Connie Eden. 155: t. Lillian Kemp; b. Bachrach. 156-157: Mark Stephensen/Westlight Backgrounds. 158: Steve Smith. 180-181: m. H.I.Smith, courtesy of Department Library Sciences, American Museum of Natural History. 182-183: Smithsonian Institution National Numismatic Collection. 184-185: Museum of Modern Art. 186: Barry Lobdell. 216-217: © Ted Horowitz/The Stock Market. **Glossary:** G0: Stephen Wilkes/The Image Bank; Superstock; Bob Croxford/The Stock Market. G1: James Carmichael/The Image Bank; Bob Burch/Bruce Coleman; Rod Planck/Photo Researchers. G2: David Young/Wolff/Photo Edit. G4: Charles Gupton/Uniphoto. G6: Bob Daemmrich/The Image Works. G8: Bob Daemmrich/Stock Boston. G9: Bruce Forster/Tony Stone Images. G10: Bob Daemmrich/The Image Works. G13: Mark Reinstein/Uniphoto. G16: J. Guichard/Sygma. G18: John Elk III/Bruce Coleman. G22: Superstock. G24: Ariel Skelley/Stock Market. G25: J.C. Carton/Bruce Coleman. G27: Lee Foster/Bruce Coleman.